# PONDS

### AND

# STREAMS

# PONDS

### AND

# STREAMS

## A NATURE
## GUIDE

### JOHN CLEGG

**The Crowood Press**

John Clegg has been curator of many natural history museums, including Haslemere Educational Museum, Torquay Museum and the Gilbert White Museum at Selborne. He is author of several natural history books, among them *Freshwater Life* and *The Observer's Book of Pond Life*.

First published in 1985 by
The Crowood Press
Ramsbury, Marlborough,
Wiltshire SN8 2HE

Reprinted in paperback 1989

British Library Cataloguing in Publication Data

Clegg, John, 1909–
    (British Naturalists' Association guide to ponds and streams). Ponds and streams
    1. Great Britain. Ponds and streams. Freshwater organisms
    I. (British Naturalists' Association guide to ponds and streams)
    I. Title II. British Naturalists' Association
    574.92'9'41

    ISBN 1–85223–233–1

**Acknowledgements**
The author wishes to thank Carole Pugh for the care she took in drawing the diagrams in Chapter 5; also, Ron Freethy of the British Naturalists' Association and Peter Leek of the Crowood Press for much help and advice during the writing of this book.

Design by Vic Giolitto

Typeset by Quadraset Limited, Midsomer Norton, Bath, Avon
Printed in Spain by Graficromo s.a., Cordoba

# Contents

# FOREWORD

Since 1905 the British Naturalists' Association has provided opportunities for beginners and more advanced students of natural history to rub shoulders with experts, both amateur and professional.

Throughout this time its magazine, *Country-Side*, and its local, regional and national meetings have fostered the collection and sharing of knowledge concerning the rocks, soils, plants and animals which make up our living landscape. Essential in this process of national learning and the spreading of awareness about wildlife has been the publication of many identification keys – keys to groups like lichens, plant galls, harvestmen and spiders, which though present and often abundant in most habitats were at one time frequently overlooked or wrongly ignored, because there was no way in, no key to unlock the doors of enquiry. In the same way, the Association's pamphlets entitled 'Let's begin the study of . . .' helped pioneer many branches of field science.

At last, some of that knowledge, the fruit of all those eighty years of unique experience, is now made public in this superb series of books. Habitat by habitat, all is revealed.

Most of my own knowledge of plants and animals was gained in the field by walking with and listening to the 'ologists', the experts in each subject – bryology, ornithology, algology etc, etc. Each trip was an occasion to be remembered thanks to the personal anecdotes and sheer enthusiasm of people who had all the facts at their fingertips and who loved the subject of their expertise.

If you can't go on such trips, these books are the next best thing. Open up the pages and you can almost smell the sweet or rotten smell of a river, see the rooks flying from the beech hangers, and hear the warm buzz of summer insects or the crisp crackle of a winter morning.

If I may be allowed one personal reminiscence. I can remember following John Clegg down to the ponds in the grounds of Haslemere Educational Museum, where he was then curator. *Stratiotes aloides* (water soldier), *Nepa cinerea* (the water scorpion), *Hydrocharis morsus ranae* (frogbit), *Gunnera manicata* (the giant prickly rhubarb from South America). . . . This was the first time I was ever shown these things and I will never forget either the experience or the names.

I am grateful to John Clegg and all the others who led me along the many paths of natural history and to a very full and worthwhile life. I am grateful too to all the officers and members of the British Naturalists' Association, both past and present, for everything they have done and are doing to share their knowledge and wonder of life.

What a super series of books! The only problem is what is the B.N.A. going to do to celebrate its centenary?

**David Bellamy**

*President of the Youth Section of*
*the British Naturalists' Association*
Bedburn, County Durham

# British Naturalists' Association

The British Naturalists' Association has existed since 1905, when E. Kay Robinson founded the B.N.A.'s journal *Country-Side* and groups of readers began to hold meetings which gave amateur naturalists an opportunity to meet experts and to discuss topics of mutual interest with them. It is this network of branches all over Britain that forms the basis of the B.N.A. New members are always welcome and enquiries regarding membership should be addressed to Mrs June Pearton, 48 Russell Way, Higham Ferrers, Northamptonshire NN9 8EJ.

During its eighty years of existence many distinguished naturalists and public figures have been associated with the B.N.A. At present the President is Lord Skelmersdale, the President of the Youth Section is David Bellamy, and R.S.R. Fitter, Eric Hosking, Alfred Leutscher, Professor Kenneth Mellanby, Angela Rippon, Sir Peter Scott, Professor T.R.E. Southwood, Sir George Taylor and H.J. Wain are Vice-Presidents of the Association.

*Country-Side* appears four times a year and publishes articles about every aspect of natural history. Contributions, including photographs and drawings, should be addressed to Ron Freethy, The Editor, *Country-Side*, Thorneyholme Hall, Roughlee, Nr Burnley, Lancashire BB12 9LH.

# 1 WATER

The one feature common to both ponds and streams is that they contain fresh water. But what is this substance? It is not pure water, in the sense that distilled water is, and certainly the great variety of plants and animals found in ponds and streams could not exist in pure water. But one of the most remarkable properties of water is its ability to dissolve more substances (both gases and solids) than any other liquid, including those needed by living things

The most important of the gases are oxygen and carbon dioxide. It might be thought that, since water is a chemical compound of oxygen and hydrogen, aquatic organisms could obtain all the oxygen they need from the water itself. But this is not so. What they must have is free oxygen *dissolved* in water. Most of this oxygen is absorbed from the atmosphere at the surface. Rain also dissolves the gas as it falls through the air and some reaches ponds and streams either directly from rain falling into the water or indirectly from surface drainage passing over rocks or through the surrounding soil.

Carbon dioxide is needed by plants to carry out the process of photosynthesis whereby the green pigment chlorophyll which gives them their colour, using absorbed energy from sunlight, combines the carbon in the gas with the hydrogen in water to form the carbohydrate part of their food, sugar. In the process oxygen is released and in freshwater habitats augments the supply from the other sources described above.

Carbon dioxide from the atmosphere dissolves readily at the water surface and more is derived in solution from ground water, but most is already in a pond or stream as a result of the decomposition process which breaks down the remains of dead plants and animals into simpler substances. Some carbon dioxide is stored up in chemical compounds called carbonates, which can be released in certain circumstances. Finally, all living things give out carbon dioxide in their respiration.

As well as oxygen and carbon dioxide, water in its journey to a pond or stream dissolves many solid materials, including chemical compounds of calcium, sodium, magnesium, potassium, phosphorus, nitrogen, iron and other less well known elements. Readers who are gardeners will recognise some of these substances as constituents of the fertilisers they use for their plants. They have the same function in ponds and streams. As we shall see later, other less desirable substances can also be dissolved in the water that may be harmful to living organisms.

It will be obvious that the geology of the land where a pond or stream is situated or from which it receives its supply of water has a considerable influence on the mineral substances reaching it. Where there are mainly soft sedimentary rocks from which compounds of calcium such as calcium carbonate (lime) and magnesium carbonate can be dissolved, the waters will support a more abundant life than when hard volcanic rocks, which dissolve much less easily, predominate.

The transparency of water is also an important feature, since sunlight can penetrate to a depth of a few metres in clear water, enabling the plants to carry out photosynthesis. The quality of the light decreases gradually with the depth as the red and orange rays, those most useful in photosynthesis, are absorbed to a greater degree than the green and blue. Nevertheless, water plants can thrive on the bottom of most ponds, though only in the shallow margins or upper layers of a large lake. All animals are dependent on plants for food, either directly or indirectly, so the transparency of water is important to them, too. Also, it enables them to see where food is and spot predators that might attack them.

Another important characteristic of water is that it is slow to heat up and slow to cool down, so that plants and animals are not subjected to the same extremes of temperature as those on land. That is not all though, for when water cools it behaves in a truly astonishing manner. Usually as substances cool they become smaller in volume and therefore denser. Water does indeed behave in this way until it cools to a temperature of 4°C (39·2°F), when, instead of contracting, it begins to expand and becomes lighter, continuing to do so until it reaches freezing point 0°C (32°F). After reaching 4°C, therefore, the coldest water in a pond floats to the surface, where it freezes, and the ice forms a blanket between the air and the water beneath, preventing it from freezing. It is rare in Britain for a pond to freeze deeper than a few inches and in winter the living things, including such relatively large animals as fish, remain safely at the bottom at a water temperature of about 4°C.

Let us look at the matter of density more closely. Water is more than 700 times denser than air and gives all-round support to objects in it. The very small microscopic plants and animals can float effortlessly as plankton. Larger water plants, supported as they are on all sides, remain upright without the need for the strong, woody tissue that land plants must have. The next time you lift a plant out of a pond or aquarium, notice how limp it is. The larger animals do not have to support their own weight and can move easily, swimming with quite slender limbs, although those that need to swim quickly to catch their prey may have legs fringed with stiff bristles to serve as oars and sometimes have streamlined bodies to reduce friction. Soft-bodied animals such as hydras and moss animals, anchored as they are to stones or plants, can stretch their bodies in any direction without effort in search of prey.

At the surface water has a layer which, although not differing chemically from the rest, is in a state of tension and acts like an elastic skin able to support small objects above and below it. It is easy to show the presence of the skin by gently lowering a needle on to the surface of water in a tumbler. Although made of steel, which is heavier than water, the needle floats. This surface film is important to small animals such as pond-skaters, which can walk on it as confidently as if it were ice. It also enables those that need to take in air at the surface, such as the larvae of gnats, to support themselves from the underside of the film.

# 2  PONDS AND STREAMS

## Ponds

There have been many attempts to define what is a pond but none has been totally satisfactory, for the word is commonly applied to a great variety of expanses of water. The essential features, though, are that a pond should be a small body of still water, usually shallow enough for water plants to grow over most of its bed. Thus the so-called 'lakes' in town parks or in the grounds of country estates are in a biological sense just as much ponds as the more traditional farm or village ponds.

The majority of ponds are the result of man's activities, yet the part they have played in our social history has never been adequately appreciated.

A source of water is the first essential for any human settlement. Where streams and rivers are few, as on the chalk downlands of southern England, natural hollows in the ground where water collected were probably the first chosen sites of the early people who lived there. Much later the so-called 'dew-ponds' were constructed to supply water for sheep and cattle pastured on these chalk uplands, although dew played little if any part in renewing the water supply. The ponds were carefully sited in hollows to collect rain and surface run-off from a wide area. The bottom of a dew-pond was lined with puddled clay, with a layer of flints on top to prevent damage by the hoofs of animals. Some ponds, especially in the north of England, were built of concrete.

In lowland Britain the pond was the centre-piece of a village, as much a part of it as the village green, on which it usually stood. Originally it provided the water supply for the villagers, as well as for their livestock. Later, in larger villages, the water-cart delivered the domestic supply to houses away from the pond. A search around one of these

Ashmore, Dorset – an
early village pond

old ponds will usually reveal the remains of the pump and perhaps a well built pump-house, from which in more recent times a purer supply, from well or spring, was available.

The village pond served also to mete out justice to minor offenders of the law: they were ducked in the water, and ducking-stools can still be seen in museums. An especially fine example is in the Priory Church, Leominster. Suspected witches were also tried by being immersed in the pond. If they floated during the ordeal they were considered guilty; if they sank they were regarded as innocent, though by that time they were probably past caring! The last 'swimming' of a witch was in 1880.

Away from the village, landowners built field-ponds to serve the dual purpose of watering their grazing animals and draining their land. Such ponds are often sited at the junction of several fields. Other ponds were the result of digging for peat or gravel or for clay needed to improve soil being cultivated elsewhere, since the cavities produced by such excavations soon filled with water. Sometimes these ponds were suitable as flighting ponds to attract wildfowl for the pot or served as fish-ponds. Stew-ponds, in which carp and other coarse fish could be reared, were part of every big estate and religious house – providing a welcome change of diet, especially for fast-days when meat was forbidden.

Wayside ponds were vital to long-distance travellers on horseback or in carriages, as well as to drovers taking cattle or sheep to market. A less obvious use of a pond is seen in old pictures of country life where a horse and cart is stationary in the deep water, the carter apparently having a rest. Wooden cart-wheels dried out in hot weather and shrank. If they were not then soaked in water to make them swell again, the iron tyre would fall off. So a regular visit to a pond or stream was necessary.

Water power has been used by man from

Farm pond, Cheshire

earliest times and some of our most attractive ponds have come about because a good head of water was needed to work the water-wheels which turned the stones used in milling corn. Such mill-ponds still exist, although their function has ceased. In some parts of the country, notably the Weald of Surrey, Kent and Sussex, similar ponds were made by damming streams to power the tilt-hammers of early iron-forges and later to operate the huge bellows when blast-furnaces were introduced to manufacture cast-iron goods.

Unfortunately, natural ponds have largely disappeared in many parts of the country during the last few years. Piped water supplies have reached nearly every rural district and made both farm and village ponds unnecessary. Once a pond has no further use and no one has any responsibility for keeping the marginal vegetation in check, it soon begins to fill up with plants such as bulrushes. Eventually it is filled in or becomes the village rubbish-tip. Many former village ponds have

A fast stream

disappeared in road-widening schemes or the building of housing estates; and field-ponds, with government encouragement, have been filled in to facilitate mechanical farming.

Some villages have still retained their ponds as amenities – indeed, a great incentive to do so, and also to clean up ponds that had fallen into decay, was provided by the 'Save the Village Pond' campaign, which restored over two thousand ponds throughout the country between 1974 and 1977. County nature conservation trusts have also been active in restoring or saving many ponds.

The availability of modern plastic pond-liners, which have done away with the arduous work of making concrete linings, has encouraged many gardeners to add interest and beauty to their garden with small pools, in itself a valuable conservation exercise. Frogs and dragonflies, both endangered species, breed freely in garden pools and with care can be reared to maturity to make up for losses in their more usual habitats.

Sheltered as they usually are by trees or banks, ponds are almost free from the wind and wave action that makes life difficult for plants and animals living at the edge of a lake. In a shallow pond water plants thrive even in the middle, thus providing a good food supply for vegetarian animals, which in turn benefits the carnivorous animals. However, too dense a growth of plants can pose a problem – for, although plants give out oxygen during daylight hours when they are photosynthesising, they take in oxygen for respiration both day and night. It is easy to demonstrate experimentally that a weedy pond which on a sunny day is supersaturated

A slow stream

with dissolved oxygen at noon may have its oxygen supply almost completely depleted at dawn. This is a limiting factor for animals that need a good oxygen supply, such as certain fish.

Plants also restrict the free movement of water, causing the temperature to fluctuate more than in a stream or lake – and this too decreases the oxygen supply, since warm water holds less of the gas than cold water does.

Nevertheless, many ponds teem with life and representatives of almost every major division of the plant and animal kingdoms may be found in quite a small pond. Among the plants there may be examples of algae, bacteria, fungi, mosses and liverworts, ferns and their relatives, and many families of flowering plants. The animals may include Protozoa (single-celled animals), sponges, hydras, flatworms, roundworms, true worms (annelids), moss animals, snails and mussels, crustaceans, insects, spiders and mites, fish and amphibians. Details of these plants and animals will be given in succeeding chapters.

Stagnant ditches and the quieter reaches of canals have similar characteristics to ponds and often have a rich community of organisms similar to those found in ponds.

All these small freshwater habitats offer the amateur naturalist much scope for original research since they have been sadly neglected by professional biologists, who have concentrated on lakes and rivers.

## Streams

Streams are probably even more diverse than ponds. Indeed, a single stream can change its character several times as it progresses from its source to its final disappearance into a river or perhaps the sea. A torrent rushing down a mountainside bears little resemblance either in appearance or in the plants and animals living in it to its later stage as a placid stretch of water meandering over a lowland meadow. When does a stream become a river? The usual convention is to call any natural watercourse up to five metres wide a stream and anything over that width a river.

A running stream is quite a different kind of habitat for plants and animals from a still pond. The continuous, one-directional flow of water poses problems, notably the ever-present danger of being swept away downstream and generally turbulent conditions in which to live. We shall see later how these problems are coped with.

Like ponds, many streams and rivers have been affected by man's activities. For centuries they have been a dumping-ground for waste material of all kinds, especially domestic sewage and effluents from industrial processes. Some substances, such as water seeping from lead, copper or zinc mines, are poisonous and kill both plants and animals. Other, biological, forms of pollution, including untreated sewage, use up oxygen in the water as bacteria break it down to simpler constituents and thus reduce the oxygen con-

tent of the water below that needed by some fish and the invertebrate animals on which they feed; they either have to move downstream or die. Even treated sewage contains chemical substances, especially nitrates and phosphates, which are also present in garden fertilisers, and can fertilise the water in a stream, encouraging excessive growth of algae, which trap silt washed down by the stream, cover the water plants and, when they die down, cause silting of an otherwise clear stream. When conditions become bad, growths of 'sewage fungus' appear – a mass of bacteria, Protozoa and fungi.

Modern agriculture, with its increasing reliance on artificial fertilisers, especially nitrates on grassland, aggravates the problem, for these substances wash out of the soil and find their way into watercourses. This cannot really be called pollution in the strict sense and the word eutrophication (from the Greek *eu*, good; *trophon*, food) is used to describe the enrichment of the water that they cause. The evidence is scum and masses of algae, especially 'blanket-weed', *Cladophora*, on the surface or bottom. In bad areas the clean water invertebrate animals decline in number and a 'pollution fauna' appears, with such animals as sludge-worms, 'bloodworms' and freshwater louse succeeding one another in abundance as one goes downstream.

Chemical sprays, used for destroying fungal diseases of crops and insect pests, can also reach rivers, as can seepage from silage and the liquid slurry from cattle kept indoors. All these can poison freshwater organisms.

*Cladophora*: an indicator of pollution

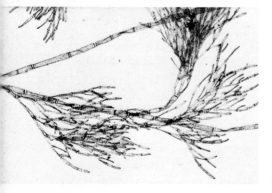

The regional names for freshwater habitats are somewhat confusing. What have been referred to in this chapter as ponds are called 'pits' in parts of Lancashire and 'tarns' in the hill country of the north of England, while a stream or brook is a 'beck' in northern England, a 'burn' in Scotland and an 'afon' in Wales and lakes are 'lochs' in Scotland, 'llyns' in Wales and 'loughs' in Ireland.

# 3  PLANT LIFE

Part of the attractiveness of a pond or stream is the waterside vegetation – tall, lush and colourful. Clearly life near the water has advantages for the plants. There is a plentiful supply of easily available nutrients in the wet ground and the reduced risk of drought ensures their survival in all but the driest summers. The species that are seen, though, are rather special, because not all plants can live in waterlogged soil. Oxygen is not as plentiful in water, even in solution, as it is in air. Most plants, even the pot plants we grow in our houses, need soil which is not water-logged but has plenty of air between the particles. If we cut sections from aquatic and waterside plants, we find that the stems, roots and leaves have large spaces between their cells in which air can be stored. These spaces frequently join up with those in the rest of the plant so that air reaches every part. Marsh plants, too, usually have large leaves from which excess moisture can be passed out through breathing holes called stomata.

**Marsh plants**  Typical of these marsh plants is the lovely marsh marigold, or kingcup, which brightens up the countryside in spring with its showy yellow flowers. These have no petals, but the sepals change colour from green to golden yellow as they develop.

Even more showy is the yellow iris, or yellow flag, with its long sword-like leaves and groups of two or three brilliant yellow flowers. Later in the year come the frothy flowers of meadowsweet, the rose-coloured flowers of great willow-herb, or codlins-in-cream, purple loosestrife and bur-marigolds. Rushes and sedges are much in evidence around the waterside.

**Swamp plants**  The marshy area merges into a more swampy region where the ground

Marsh marigold

Yellow iris

Great reedmace or bulrush

is covered with water except in very dry weather, although it is not always easy to make a fine dividing line between the two zones because in times of flood the swamp invades the marsh and in dry weather the reverse happens. So some 'marsh species' may occur in the swamp and 'swamp plants' in the marsh.

The plants characteristic of the swamp zone are tall, with narrow leaves, their height enabling them to cope better with rapid changes of water level and the leaves offering little resistance to strong winds. Perhaps the best known is the bulrush, or greater reedmace, which may attain a height of over six feet. With its large brown poker-shaped seed-head, it is a familiar sight in the country and a favourite of flower-arrangers. The head remains aloft after the leaves have died down in winter and only disappears in spring, when the fluffy seeds have been dispersed by wind. A smaller and rarer species is the lesser reedmace. In this plant the male and female parts of the flower-spike which becomes the seed-head are separated by a length of stem, whereas in the larger species they are continuous.

In larger ponds and sometimes along slow streams, even where the water is brackish, the common reed forms dense communities. It is characteristic of swamp plants to advance into the water by means of long submerged horizontal stems called rhizomes buried in the mud. At intervals along them grow up strong shoots so that in a short time a dense community is formed which can take over a small pond very quickly. Many a gardener who has added a single bulrush plant to his garden pool has had cause to regret it when all he has left of his pond is a mass of tall vegetation, with a solid mat of rhizomes which are extremely hard to dig out.

The decay of leaves in the autumn and the collection of debris around the base of these tall swamp plants in time can raise the level of the bed of a natural pond or stream until only a damp patch shows where there was once an attractive stretch of water.

Less troublesome plants in the swampy region, especially where the vegetation is not so dense, are clumps of branched bur-reed, with flower-heads made up of tiny flowers clustered together into a round ball. Water plantain, with large oval leaves and a tall flowering branch of pale lilac flowers standing erect, mingles with the beautiful flowering rush, one of our most handsome waterside plants, with its large umbel of rose-pink flowers. Smaller plants may include watercresses, water parsnips, brooklime and water mint, the last making its presence known by its characteristic smell.

**Water plants** The remaining flowering plants to be described are the true aquatics, which are unable to live on land. Although they are descended from land plants, they have become ideally adapted for living in their new habitat. Most have lost the tough supporting tissues that land plants need to keep them upright and are fragile, with pale green stems and leaves which have a thin epidermis, or skin, that enables them to absorb not only the oxygen and carbon dioxide they need, but also mineral salts in solution from the water, over the whole surface of the plant. Roots still exist on some of them, serving as anchors and also taking up nutrients. Stomata, the pores through which plants usually exchange gases with the air, are not present on submerged leaves but are located on the upper surface of floating leaves. Air spaces are large and abundant in these plants.

Pollination is usually difficult in totally submerged plants, but they propagate luxuriantly by vegetative means and some manage to exist over the winter by producing winter-buds, packed with starch, from which new plants can arise the following year. Others have rhizomes, as already described, and some merely produce a special compact portion of a stem or tip of a shoot which survives the winter in the warmer water at the bottom of the pond.

Water plants can be divided into several groups depending on their mode of life:
1 plants rooted in the mud, with leaves either floating at the surface or standing out of the water;
2 plants floating freely at the surface, with no roots attached to the mud;
3 plants totally submerged and rooted in the mud.

**Floating-leaved plants** Undoubtedly, the best known of the first group are the waterlilies. Two species are common: the white water-lily and the yellow water-lily, distinguished when not in flower by the round leaves of the former and the oval leaves of the yellow species. The least water-lily, which also has yellow flowers but is much smaller, occurs only in lakes in Scotland, the Midlands and Wales, but it does hybridise with the yellow water-lily.

The leaves of water-lilies have a waxy surface which repels water and prevents them from becoming waterlogged. The stems are long and flexible enough to adapt to changes in depth and movement of the water. The stomata, as mentioned previously, are only on the upper surface of the leaves. The flowers are pollinated by insects and the large fruits containing many seeds are formed in the autumn. Those of the yellow water-lily float away for some distance before breaking open and liberating the seeds, but the fruit of the white water-lily splits under water to release the seeds to float away and disperse. The plants overwinter by means of rhizomes, which form a dense mat in the mud. In some countries the rhizomes are dug out for food, as they are rich in starch.

Resembling a small water-lily is the fringed water-lily, but it is not a true relative and is more closely related to the gentians. The fringe is on the edges of the five petal-like

**Above** Common reed

**Left** Branched bur-reed in fruit

**Opposite (top)** Floating-leaved and emergent pond plants

**Opposite (below)** Fringed water-lily

lobes of the yellow flowers. The round leaves are purple underneath.

The white flowers of the water crowfoots cover the surface of ponds and streams during May and June. They belong to the buttercup family and there are several species, which are not always easy to distinguish, especially as their form varies with the depth of water they are in or the speed of the current in streams. Most have two kinds of leaves, the floating leaves being lobed and the submerged ones finely dissected, but other species have only one type of leaf. The long strands of river crowfoot floating on the current of a clear stream make a lovely sight. Although there has been much discussion as to why water plants have two or more distinct types of leaves, there can be no doubt that in streams the finely dissected type offers less resistance to the flow of water and is less likely to cause the plant to be uprooted than flat leaves would.

A plant with no less than three types of leaf is arrowhead. The characteristic leaves from which it gets its name stand out above the water and can hardly be mistaken. The first leaves, which arise in spring from a tuber in the mud, are ribbon-like and translucent. These are followed by narrow, oval floating leaves, then finally the typical arrow-shaped aerial leaves appear. The white flowers, with purple centres, are carried in a cluster at the top of a long stem.

The floating oval leaves of broad-leaved pondweed often cover the greater part of a pond, but this plant also has narrow submerged leaves. The green flower-spikes can easily be overlooked. There are many species of pondweed and they can be found in bog pools and slow streams as well as ponds. Some are completely submerged and not easily seen. The floating leaves of these plants – indeed, all floating leaves – are a good place to look for the egg-masses of snails and insects, colonies of moss animals and the oval cases of the caterpillars of china-mark moths. An oval hole at the edge of a leaf indicates that caterpillars are in the vicinity, the missing piece of leaf will be found on the underside of a neighbouring leaf, with a caterpillar in between.

**Floating plants with unanchored roots** have, of course, severed all contact with land. Good examples are the various species of duckweed, whose tiny green leaves cover the water surface like a scum. When a pond is covered with duckweed it usually means the water is rich in nutrients, perhaps due to drainage from a manure heap or cesspool. The commonest species is lesser duckweed. Its 'leaves', or more correctly thalli, are about 2mm to 4mm (⅛ to ³/₁₆ inch) across and each has a single root hanging down into the water, helping to stabilise the plant like a keel and to absorb nutrients. Greater duckweed is about twice the size and each of the thalli, which are purple underneath, has several long roots below, while the thalli of fat duckweed have thick, spongy tissue beneath them.

Ivy-leaved duckweed, on the other hand, does not float on the surface but lives totally submerged just below the surface. The individual thalli are long and pointed, the ivy-leaf effect occurring when two new thalli develop from an old one. The smallest flowering plant in the world is a native duckweed, *Wolffia*, which measures only 0.5mm to 1mm across and has no roots.

Duckweed flowers are greenish and minute – but they are rarely seen in Britain and reproduction is usually of a non-sexual nature, new thalli being formed on opposite sides of the original ones.

A much larger floating plant is frogbit, which has leaves like those of a small water-lily. It often grows in abundance, with many individual plants close together, their runners forming a solid mat. The white three-petalled flowers appear in profusion in July and August both in ponds and ditches. On the creeping submerged stems winter-buds are

Winter buds of frogbit developing in the spring

produced, consisting of tightly packed leaves, rich in starch. These drop off the old plant in autumn and remain in the mud until spring growth starts, the starch is used up and air spaces appear in the leaves. The now light winter-bud then rises to the surface and develops into a new plant.

Quite unlike frogbit in appearance but belonging to the same family is water soldier. The name presumably refers to the sharp sword-like leaves which form a rosette branching out compactly from a central stem. These are extremely effective in keeping the surface of the water above them clear of other plants and enable dense stands of water soldier to colonise wide areas. In one season it can take over a small pond.

Water soldier is not a common plant and is more likely to be seen in eastern counties of Britain than elsewhere. For most of the year it is totally submerged just below the surface, but at flowering time (about June) the plant rises to allow the white flowers to appear above the surface – a wasted exercise, as only female plants occur in Britain, so no seeds can be set. Long roots hang down in the water, sometimes ending in a kind of pad which rests on or in the mud. This pad seems to be important in keeping the plant in a vertical position; indeed, if it is removed by accident, the plant becomes very unstable. When the flowers die, the plant sinks down in the water. Throughout the summer young plants

develop from buds on runners from the parent plant, but in autumn these buds develop slowly and serve the purpose of winter-buds, although remaining on the parent plant.

In the bladderworts, small bladders are borne on the finely dissected submerged leaves and when a small animal, such as a water flea, touches the trigger hairs at the entrance to the bladder, a trap-door springs open and the unfortunate victim is swept inside in a rush of water. The trap-door then closes and in due course the animal dies and its liquid remains are absorbed through hairs inside the bladder. The plant is therefore able to grow in water which may lack essential nutrients in solution.

The yellow flowers of the bladderworts appear on long stems above the surface in late summer and are often the only clue to the presence of the plants, which are otherwise totally submerged. Oval or egg-shaped winter-buds are produced in autumn, or earlier when the plants are in waters particularly poor in nutrients. They remain on the shoots of the parent plant until spring, but break away then to become new plants.

Two species of hornwort complete the tally of floating plants. Their stout stems look like green bottle-brushes, with whorls of fine leaves at intervals along the stem. The finely divided leaflets of these submerged plants

**Above** Water crowfoot in a stream          **Below** Arrowhead and frogbit

Water soldier

offer a large surface area for the absorption of gases and minerals from the water – important in plants like these which have no stomata and must take in all they need all over their surface.

The commoner species (sometimes called the rigid hornwort) has a tougher, brittle feel about it and its leaves are forked into two points. The soft hornwort, on the other hand, as its name implies, is more delicate and usually lighter in colour, with leaves forked into three points. Both live in still water and do not seem to object to brackish water. In sheltered, darker places they seem to grow into compacter plants and if brought into a well lighted aquarium soon become lank and drawn out. Flowers do not appear every year, but when present they are in the axils of the leaves. Both male and female flowers are produced on the same plant below the water level. The stamens of the male flowers float to the surface in late summer, and release their pollen, which then sinks to fertilise the female flowers. The hornworts, therefore, have become more completely adapted to living in water than any of the plants that have been mentioned. At first, when the plants are seen upright in the water, they appear to have roots. However, the small light-coloured shoots which sometimes grow from the lower branches and even penetrate the mud a little are not true roots, although they do serve as anchors and, it is believed, even absorb some mineral nutrients from the mud. No winter-buds are produced as in this unusual and interesting plant seed is set which germinates at the bottom of the water, the young plant then rising to the surface. As they become older they tend to sink lower in the water.

**Submerged rooted plants** The last group of aquatic flowering plants are those that are both submerged and rooted in the mud. Canadian waterweed, a favourite of aquarists because of its good oxygenating qualities, is

Canadian waterweed

level at which only a limited number of plants can thrive.

Canadian waterweed survives the winter by developing shoots with tightly packed leaves which remain dormant until spring, when they develop normally. The tiny greenish-purple flowers appear on the surface of the water from May to October on long thin stalks, which may be up to 30cm (nearly 12 inches) in length.

Water-milfoils are graceful plants living in both still and slow-moving, but usually alkaline, waters. The upright stems bear whorls of feathery leaves at intervals. In the commoner spiked water-milfoil there are usually four leaves in a whorl; the rarer whorled water-milfoil usually has five leaves in a whorl. The small flowers, dull-reddish in the spiked and greenish-yellow in the whorled water-milfoil, with males above and females below, are held out of the water and are wind pollinated. Whorled water-milfoil makes sure of surviving winter, for not only does it set seed but it has a rhizome and also produces winter-buds in autumn, which become detached from the parent plant. Winter-buds are absent in the spiked water-milfoil.

It is difficult to decide in which group of aquatic plants to place the water-starworts, several species of which occur in Britain in both still and running waters. They are both submerged and rooted, but some (including the common water-starwort) can exist perfectly well on mud, even on muddy tracks in woodland, away from water. The various species are difficult to identify because the leaves vary in form, depending on whether they are in still or flowing water and also whether they are floating in the water, submerged, or on land. The tiny fruits are an important aid to identification, but the plants do not always flower. When present, the male and female flowers are both green and are carried on the same plant. They are borne in the axils of the cluster of leaves floating on the surface. These leaves are star-shaped and

probably the best known and most widely distributed in ponds or slow-moving streams. It is remarkable, firstly because it is an alien plant, a native of North America, and secondly because there is only one record of a male plant being found in Britain and so no seed can be set. The plant is an excellent example of the success of vegetative reproduction in water plants. The stems are very brittle and any small fragment that breaks off can develop into a new plant. It is an interesting thought that all the specimens we see today are offshoots of the original few plants that were introduced about 1840. Their spectacular spread in a few years caused much concern as they colonised streams, rivers and canals at an alarming rate, choking the waterways and making boating, fishing and swimming impossible. After a time the luxuriant growth declined and by 1880 Canadian waterweed settled down as a normal occupant of suitable aquatic habitats. Even now, though, it is characteristic of the plant when introduced to a new habitat to have a period of luxuriant growth before gradually declining to a more stable condition.

Presumably, such growth reduces some essential mineral nutrients in the water to a account for the common name of the plant.

Water-starworts have no special provision for surviving winter; they merely remain at the bottom of the water, where they are almost always safe from frost.

In the space available it has not been possible to mention all the flowering plants found in and around ponds and streams. A selection of those characteristic of the main groups has been described to illustrate their variety and how they have adapted to their environment. The reader is referred to some of the books in the list at the end of the book for more detailed information about the plants themselves.

Flowering plants, alien though they may be to fresh water, are nevertheless important in the economy of pond and stream, both when they are alive and after they have died. Their leaves and stems provide food for herbivorous animals and the dead leaves, not only of plants around the habitat but those blown in from trees and shrubs some distance away, are now known to be an essential part of the food of some animals, especially when broken down by moulds and bacteria. The plants in the water also augment the oxygen supply during photosynthesis and give shelter and support for the eggs, larvae, pupae and adult stages of a great variety of animals. A pond or stream with a rich assemblage of flowering plants is usually the place where most animal life will be found.

# Non-flowering plants

The plants described so far have all been flowering or seed plants, although it is not always possible to see either their flowers or seeds because, living in water, some have abandoned that method of reproduction. We now turn to the equally large group of non-flowering plants, which includes representatives of bacteria, fungi, algae, mosses and liverworts, and the ferns and horsetails. These are less familiar than flowering plants, and

often a microscope is required to see and study them; nevertheless, they play an important part in freshwater habitats.

**Bacteria** Bacteria are one of the principal agents in the breakdown or decomposition of dead plant and animal remains and the recycling of their complex organic substances into simpler chemical compounds which can be used again by living plants. Several groups of bacteria are engaged in this process, each in turn simplifying the material produced so that it becomes usable. First the proteins of the decaying material are converted into ammonium compounds and these are changed into nitrites and finally into nitrates. Nitrates are needed in large quantities by plants. Oxygen is used up in these processes and when large amounts of decomposing material in a pond are converted there may be a serious depletion of the oxygen supply available to the animals.

Although bacteria are too small to be seen individually with the naked eye, evidence of their presence or activities can sometimes be seen – or smelled – in ponds or streams. Legends of 'Will-o'-the-wisp' or of 'Jack-o'-lantern', a flame dancing over the water, have been part of country folklore from time immemorial. The phenomenon is due to the spontaneous ignition of marsh gas, or methane, produced by bacterial breakdown and decomposition of organic remains in the mud. Less spectacular are bubbles of gas rising through the water from the mud and giving rise to a smell of rotten eggs. This is hydrogen sulphide, or sulphuretted hydrogen. Sulphur bacteria can break it down and store the sulphur temporarily in their cells, ultimately converting it into the sulphates needed by plants. Roundish masses of sulphur bacteria can also be seen sometimes in the water, giving it a purplish tint.

In stagnant ditches and swampy stretches of water a rust-red deposit on stones or plants indicates the activities of iron bacteria. These convert iron salts in the water to obtain oxygen and accumulate the 'rust' (ferric oxide) in the sheath surrounding them. Some iron bacteria cause problems in water supplies by coating the inside of iron pipes and even blocking them completely.

Brown fluffy masses attached to plants in boggy pools are also evidence of another iron bacterium, called the 'ochre bacterium'. An oily film on the surface of water can also indicate the presence of bacteria.

Bacteria, including those which cause disease such as the typhoid bacillus, can enter ponds and streams in water from the land or in sewage. *Escherichia coli*, a normal bacterium of the human intestine, is sometimes used as an indicator of such pollution.

**Fungi (water moulds)**  Like bacteria, fungi have no chlorophyll and cannot make their food from simple chemical substances as other plants do. They either have to live as parasites on living plants or animals, or as saprophytes on dead and decaying organisms.

In water the fungi are represented by water moulds and the saprophytes among them break down dead organic matter and recycle it into simpler chemicals which can be used by plants.

Although water moulds are small, some can be seen with the naked eye – for example the common fungus *Saprolegnia*, which attacks both goldfish and other fish kept in aquaria and garden ponds. The whitish tufts consist of many filaments on the ends of which develop reproductive organs, club-shaped sporangia and round oogonia. The sporangia produce free-swimming spores which settle on any suitable medium and develop into new moulds. The oogonia contain resting spores which can survive adverse conditions and germinate later. Forms of *Saprolegnia* attack both living and dead organisms and, since spores are always present in the water, any organic material soon becomes a suitable medium on which water moulds can grow.

The group called the hypomycetes feed on dead leaves or other parts of trees and shrubs that have fallen or been blown into the water and are especiall, active in fast streams where oxygen is plentiful. The spores of these moulds have long arms which anchor them to the plant material even in turbulent conditions. With the aid of a simple microscope, they can be found in great numbers in autumn and winter in the foam beneath rapids and small waterfalls. The plant material is rapidly attacked by the moulds and soon decomposes. It is now known that this source of decaying vegetation is a very important part of the food supply for small grazing animals such as the freshwater shrimp, and thus indirectly the fish which feed on it.

More primitive water moulds are the chytrids, which include both parasites and saprophytes. They attack algae and microscopic animals, sometimes on such a large scale that their populations are drastically reduced.

**Algae**  Algae are widespread and abundant on land, as plankton and seaweeds in the sea and in fresh water. Their spores are always in

Water mould, *Saprolegnia*, on eggs of the brown trout

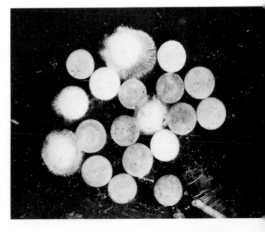

Planktonic algae and rotifers

the air or water and rapidly develop into plants wherever they find a suitable medium, as anyone can see by leaving a small vessel of rainwater in the open air in good light for a few days. It soons becomes green with algae.

Some algae are minute and consist of only a single cell. Others are aggregations of cells, form into long filaments of cells, or have a more complex structure of many cells. The ways in which algae reproduce are diverse and often complex, but always fascinating and often breathtaking in their beauty.

Although freshwater algae are, in general, small, some of the marine species – the seaweeds – are many metres in length.

All algae have chlorophyll and are therefore able to make food with the aid of sunlight from carbon dioxide and water. Mineral nutrients are absorbed through their cell walls. The abundance of algae in fresh waters, particularly those free-floating in the plankton, even in rivers and streams, makes them of great importance as primary food producers (comparable with the grasses on land) and as the first links in the food chain of freshwater animals. Their contribution to the oxygen concentration of the water by their photosynthesis must be considerable.

In some groups of algae the chlorophyll is obscured by other pigments so that the plants are not always green. These colour differences, although correlated with other characteristics in the classification of algae, serve as a convenient basis for the descriptions of the main groups below.

**Blue-green algae** These are the most primitive algae and are considered to be closer to bacteria than to other algae. Their cells have no nucleus and the pigments are distributed throughout the whole cell and are not held in special 'chloroplasts' as in other algae. There is no sexual reproduction and multiplication is usually by simple cell division. Some

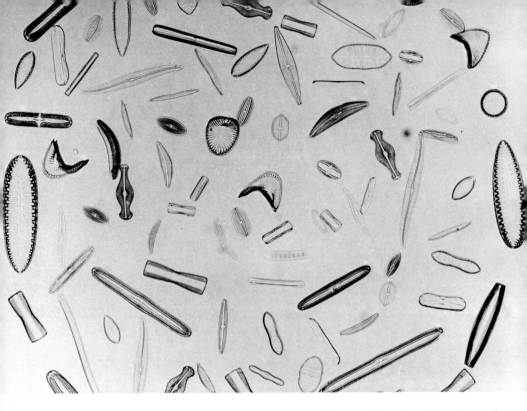

Freshwater diatoms

blue-greens are single-celled, others grow end to end in long filaments or colonies. The colours vary between blue-green, blue, yellow, red and violet, depending on the species and the habitat in which they live.

Blue-green algae are more in evidence in late summer when some of them increase greatly in numbers and, buoyed up by gas within the cells, float to the surface to form a scum, or 'water bloom'. In some parts of the country this phenomenon is called the 'breaking of the meres'. Fish and other smaller animals in the water can be killed by the poisonous substances produced at this time, and birds and animals drinking the water may die, too. Blue-green algae in human drinking water, even in minute quantities, can produce an unpleasant taste or smell.

In ponds and ditches bluey-green slime on stones or floating objects is usually evidence of the presence of *Oscillatoria*; round lumps of greenish-blue jelly up to 25mm (1 inch) across in ponds and streams are masses of *Nostoc* (which can also be seen on garden soil); dark-green masses of jelly on submerged water plants in streams are probably *Rivularia*.

**Yellow-green algae** The best known group included in this major division of the algae are the diatoms, exquisite microscopic objects which have attracted the attention of naturalists ever since they were first revealed by early microscopists. Details of the ornamentation of the cell wall, with its fine lines, punctuations and pores, became a challenge to lens-makers and microscopists alike in testing their ability to make them visible.

Unusually in plants, the cell wall in diatoms is made not of cellulose but of silica, so each diatom is, in effect, a tiny glass box with a deep lid, containing the protoplasm. When growth is active and the contents outgrow the container, the two parts of the box separate to become new individuals. Multiplication in this way is usually rapid in spring and early summer, and in spite of their tough flinty shells diatoms are food for many of the smaller aquatic animals. This rapid reproduction presents problems for water authorities, for in reservoirs a great increase in diatoms can block the filters in public supplies.

When diatoms die the 'shells' accumulate at the bottom of the water and in some parts of the world have built up huge deposits of almost pure silica. These have been exploited for industrial use as diatomite, or kieselguhr, of value as a filtration aid in many industrial processes, as a filler in paints and varnishes, and in insulation materials.

Diatoms are too small to be seen without a microscope but evidence of their presence is a brown, slimy covering on stones in streams. Water plants, too, often have a brownish coating of attached diatoms. Most species, though, are free-floating in the plankton not only in the relatively still waters of lakes and ponds but – remarkably – in the running waters of rivers and streams, where concentrations of five million per litre have been recorded in the spring maximum. These were mostly of the Centric group of diatoms, with a disc-like shape. The other group of Pennate diatoms, which are boat-shaped, seem to be less well represented in running waters.

Also included in the yellow-green algae are several well known species which can live not only in the water but on mud nearby. *Botrydium* dots the surface of the mud in and around shallow ponds with tiny green balls. *Vaucheria* is found in dark-green masses of filaments, rough to the touch, on mud or damp earth.

**Green algae** In this large group the plants are clear green in colour, with no masking of the chlorophyll. They include a wide variety of well known forms, often of great beauty.

Some are single-celled, others grow in long filaments and a few form colonies in the shape of a hollow sphere. From the bewildering number only one or two of general interest can be mentioned.

One of the smallest and simplest is *Chlorella*, a single-celled alga found abundantly in waters rich in organic matter, but its importance is that it also lives inside some of the aquatic animals that will be mentioned later (including a protozoan, a hydra, a flatworm and a freshwater sponge), giving them their characteristic green colour. This is an example of symbiosis – two organisms living in partnership for their mutual good. The alga derives food materials in the form of carbon dioxide, nitrates and phosphates from the waste products of the animal's life processes, while the animal obtains oxygen from the photosynthesis of the alga.

Perhaps the best known of all the algae is *Spirogyra*. The superficially unattractive and slippery masses of the alga at the edge of a pond, perhaps bouyed up by oxygen bubbles in spring, give no promise of the beauty and interest of the individual filaments making up the mass when seen under a microscope. The cells in the unbranched strands are joined end to end and each has a large single nucleus. The chloroplasts containing the chlorophyll are in the form of ribbons with ragged edges wound in spirals, which give it its name. Normal growth takes place by the filaments lengthening. The cell nuclei divide into two and separate, while a wall of cellulose forms between the two new cells. The interest of *Spirogyra*, however, is in its reproduction by conjugation. Two adjoining filaments send out little projections which meet and the cell walls break down. Through the passage thus formed the contents of one pass into the other and a dark oval resting body, called a zygote, develops. This germinates in due course and a new filament grows from it.

Masses of blanket-weed, dark green in colour, seen in slow streams and rivers, have a

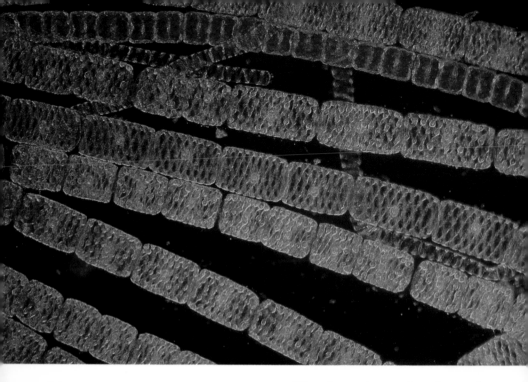

*Spirogyra*, showing nuclei

similar appearance to the masses of *Spirogyra*, but if the strands are examined closely they will be seen to be branched and they represent a more advanced stage of filamentous algae, *Cladophora*. This alga grows luxuriantly in polluted waters and is used as an indicator of such conditions, often confirmed by an unpleasant smell when the oxygen content of the water is depleted.

In spring the water in a pond or stagnant ditch seems to be a bright green colour. This is usually due to the presence of huge populations of one of the simplest of algae, *Chlamydomonas*. A microscope is needed to reveal that it is a tiny pear-shaped single cell able to swim through the water ceaselessly by means of a pair of lashes called flagella at the front end of the cell. This is no animal, however, but a plant that can swim into positions best suited to gain the maximum light to carry out photosynthesis. A red eye-spot near the flagella is able to detect light.

*Chlamydomonas* has a variety of ways of reproducing. The original cell can divide into a number of smaller ones, each with flagella, able to swim away. Minute bodies called zoospores, covered in a tough cell wall, can form in the original cell and come together outside it to form resting spores called zygotes, which when favourable conditions arise can divide and grow into new individuals. Finally, when faced with adverse conditions, *Chlamydomonas* can divide to form a large colony called the palmella or resting stage, from which free-swimming cells can emerge when conditions are favourable.

One of the most beautiful green algae is *Volvox*, a colony of *Chlamydomonas*-like individuals joined together in a common gelatinous envelope forming the outside of a perfect globe. These colonies can just be seen with the naked eye and may be so numerous in a pond as to make the water look green. To appreciate their full beauty of form and movement they must be observed under a microscope using the lowest power (an inexpensive

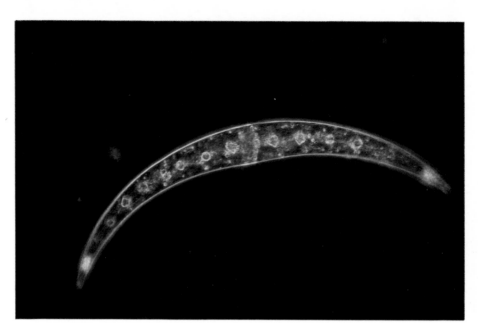

**Above** Desmid: *Closterium*

**Below** *Volvox*; the animal in the centre is the nauplius larva of a crustacean, *Diaptomus*

instrument is quite adequate). There may be up to 20,000 cells in one globe and the beating of the flagella propel it slowly through the water, rotating as it goes. Inside the hollow sphere smaller daughter colonies can be seen, which will eventually burst through the envelope to start their own existence.

Water-net, *Hydrodictyon*, is another type of algal colony, this time in the shape of a cylindrical net, the mesh of which is formed of long cells joined together.

Although totally different in appearance from *Spirogyra*, the single-celled desmids are classified with it because they employ the same method of reproduction by conjugation. Unfortunately, they cannot be seen without a microscope but under a medium-power microscope the full beauty of their form and colouring can be enjoyed.

They have a certain resemblance to diatoms, but are of varying shades of green and are further distinguished by a line or constriction across the middle of the cell which caused early students to believe that they consisted of paired cells.

Desmids occur only in fresh water and can be found in a wide range of habitats, especially the margins of small ponds and peaty pools. Some are free-floating and rise to the surface during sunlight hours so that they can sometimes be skimmed off with a fine-meshed net. Others are found among submerged plants and can be collected by drawing an open-necked bottle through the vegetation. Some species form long filaments. Common examples are the many kinds of *Closterium*, some shaped like a new moon and the lobed, almost circular, species of the genus *Micrasterias*.

**Red algae** Most of the so-called red algae are marine, but there are a few in fresh water, although the red colour is usually masked by other pigments. Most frequently seen are the species of frog-spawn alga, or bead-moss, both appropriate names as the dark-green or brown whorls of fine filaments at intervals along the branched stems look rather like frogs' eggs or beads. The plant grows attached to stones in slow-moving water. Other red algae grow as reddish or violet coverings on rocks in fast streams.

Sometimes the bottom of a bird-bath is covered with a red sediment which might be thought to be caused by red algae. This, though, is evidence of the presence of a green alga, *Haematococcus pluvialis*, related to *Chlamydomonas*, which has red pigment in addition to green. This alga also occurs in ditches and bog pools and is no doubt carried to bird-baths as a resting stage on the feet of birds.

**Stoneworts** By contrast with the algae already described, the stoneworts are enormous, sometimes reaching a length of over 30cm (12 inches), so they can easily be mistaken for flowering plants. There are over thirty species in Britain and they are found, often in dense masses, in ponds, lakes and slow streams. Some can grow in lakes well below the depth at which higher plants are able to survive and obviously do not require as much light to exist.

Stoneworts can often be recognised by their translucent green colour, although in alkaline waters they may seem rather grey, for they become coated with a layer of lime, which gives them their name. They often have a rather musty smell. Although stoneworts are usually anchored in the mud they have no true roots, only delicate structures called rhizoids. From these, whitish swellings called bulbils, rich in starch, sometimes grow and can remain in the mud until they develop into new plants in spring. Stoneworts also reproduce sexually: spherical male antheridia release a large number of small filaments, each of which contains many male cells called antherozoids which swim to fertilise the oval female oogonia. The male and female structures are close together on the same plant. The result of their union is the production of a tough-walled spore from which a new plant can arise.

Stoneworts are divided into two main groups. *Nitella* and its allies have fragile stems and small forked branches in the whorls of the leaves. *Chara* species have tougher, brittle stems which are more often encrusted with chalk, and the branchlets are never forked. The cells of these plants are very long and, when not encrusted with chalk, show clearly under a microscope the streaming of proto- plasm within the cell.

**Mosses and liverworts**  These are plants that thrive in damp places. A number of them can be found encrusting stones in and around fast streams and in the splash zones of waterfalls. Whereas a moss has a stem with leaves arranged spirally around it, most liver- worts have merely a flat frond or thallus. There are, however, leafy liverworts which have flattened leaves, but they are all in one plane and not surrounding a stem. Neither mosses nor liverworts have roots, but are attached to stones by root-like rhizoids, which play no part in absorbing water, as the root systems of higher plants do.

The great scented liverwort, so-called because it gives off a pleasant smell when bruised, occurs on wet rocks and walls near streams. Others in such situations are the common liverwort, *Marchantia*, and the wide- nerved liverwort, *Pellia epiphylla*.

More aquatic than these is floating crystal- wort, *Riccia fluitans*, the delicate pale green thalli of which float just under the surface of the water in ponds and ditches. It can also grow on wet mud, but then has star-shaped purplish rosettes.

Mosses give shelter to a variety of animals in and around streams, and if you squeeze the water out of them into a collecting tube and examine it under a microscope you will find many interesting Protozoa, rotifers and water bears.

Willow moss, *Fontinalis*

Long-beaked water feather moss, *Eurhyn- chium riparioides*, is one of the lovely feather- like mosses that seems most at home on water-splashed rocks. Bog mosses, or sphagnum, are found in abundance around all wet habitats and some actually in the water. Past accumulation of their dead remains has given us our vast deposits of peat. These plants can absorb up to twenty times their own weight of water and, as they are mildly antiseptic as well, they have served as emer- gency wound-dressings in wartime.

Willow moss, *Fontinalis antipyretica*, firmly attached to stones, grows in long strands up to a metre long in streams and still waters. It is sometimes a nuisance in watercress beds. It is strange that a plant that seems so much at home completely submerged should only produce its spore capsules when it is stranded out of water. Dried willow moss was packed around chimney flues to avoid the danger of roofs catching fire, a custom which led Linnaeus to choose the word *antipyretica* as the species name.

**Ferns and horsetails**  No native water ferns occur in Britain, but an American species,

Water horsetail

*Azolla filiculoides*, sometimes called 'fairy moss' and introduced for use as a floating plant in aquaria, has found its way into ponds and slow streams in various parts of the country. The two-lobed fronds, about 15mm (½ inch) long, vary in colour from pale green to red, the latter colour usually at the end of summer. *Azolla* spreads rapidly and can become a troublesome weed, but it is not hardy and usually dies down in winter except in very sheltered places.

Several species of horsetails grow around ponds. The tall upright stems are rough to the touch and in country districts used to be called 'scouring rushes' and were used for cleaning pots and pans. They produce cones of spore-producing bodies at the tips of some stems. The spores produce a very small frond-like structure called a prothallus, which in turn bears male and female organs. After fertilisation these give rise to new horsetail plants.

The marsh horsetail, which grows to about 60cm (2 feet), is usually found in the mud near the water; but the water horsetail, which can grow to a height of 1·5m (5 feet), lives in standing water in the swampy zone of a pond or lake, forming very dense communities.

# 4 ANIMAL LIFE

There is little doubt that all life started in the sea and some plants and animals gradually made their way via coastal swamps on to land. Their descendants are the land-living plants and animals we see today. Others, moving up rivers, became adapted over long periods of time to living in fresh water – a process which is still going on today. Those that have remained in the water are called *primarily aquatic* plants and animals. These have always lived in water of some kind and include most of the non-flowering plants that have been mentioned in previous pages and also the following groups of animals: Protozoa, or single-celled animals, sponges, hydras, flatworms, threadworms, true worms (annelids), moss animals, rotifers, crustaceans and *some* molluscs, including one or two species of water snails and mussels.

Some of the flowering plants now living in water are *secondarily aquatic*, since they deserted the land somewhat late in their evolution. Also included in this category are all aquatic insects, the water spider and water mites and the remainder of the snails.

It is helpful to remember these distinctions when considering the animals that are described in this chapter, for their origins throw light on unusual structures and behaviour in those that have taken to the water from land. The method of breathing is particularly interesting in land animals recently adapted to a permanent life in water. Creatures like beetles and bugs still breathe atmospheric air, coming to the surface to obtain it and having interesting ways of storing oxygen to make such visits less frequent. Some insects, however, are aquatic only in their early stages and seem well adapted for life in the water, absorbing oxygen through thin-walled outgrowths from the body called gills, although they are not like those of fish.

Movement through the denser medium of water was another problem that had to be faced by animals which had previously lived on land. In water bugs and water beetles it was solved by a streamlining of the body, while in other water animals the limbs are fringed with long hairs, which effectively widens them so as to provide a broad surface to the water when swimming, and in some of the dragonfly larvae jet propulsion was adopted millions of years before man invented it.

## Protozoa

The word 'Protozoa' means 'first animals', because they are not only the simplest of all animals in structure but were also the first animals to evolve on earth. It is thought that about 30,000 different kinds of Protozoa exist and are so diverse in form that some authorities consider that they should not be classified as animals but given a kingdom of their own. They are usually regarded as consisting of a single cell, but when that cell can carry out all the normal activities of a living organism – moving about in search of food, getting rid of waste products and reproducing – it seems that it might be better to consider Protozoa as non-cellular animals rather than single-celled ones.

Most Protozoa are very small – less than half a millimetre across – and therefore impossible to study without a microscope but, since they are individually far more numerous than any other animals, they must not be ignored. They are important as food for the slightly larger animals, as they contribute greatly to the plankton of the seas and all freshwater habitats. Some feed on bacteria, others help to break down organic debris and recycle it. On the other hand, some of the worst diseases of man are caused by Protozoa: sleeping sickness is caused by a flagellate *Trypanosoma*, amoebic dysentery by an amoeba, and malaria, which still affects half the world population, by a sporozoan called *Plasmodium*.

Protozoa multiply by dividing into two more individuals, but sometimes two animals come together in conjugation and after an exchange of nuclear matter separate and continue dividing in the usual way. This sexual stage is necessary as it avoids inbreeding and maintains vigour.

In the past Protozoans and other small organisms were lumped together as 'infusorians' because they appeared as if by magic in a hay infusion. This is still the best way to start a study of Protozoa. Place a small quantity of hay or other dried vegetation in a jar of rainwater and keep it for a few days in an airing cupboard. By that time a film will have formed on the surface of the water and if a little of this is examined on a glass slide under a microscope you will see that it is teeming with an exciting collection of minute living things. As the days pass some forms will be replaced by others, but most will belong to the group called ciliates discussed later in this chapter.

What is the explanation of this sudden explosion of life from dead grass? When conditions in a pond become unfavourable for Protozoa, especially when the pond dries up, these small animals can surround themselves with a resistant covering. In this 'encysted' state they can be carried long distances by the wind, settling on vegetation or in another stretch of water, where the cyst breaks up and life can start again. These minute specks of dormant life, like the spores of algae, are always in the air and no new body of water remains long without an invasion.

**Flagellates** The protozoans in this important group are so named because they have one or more whip-like 'flagella' at the front end of the body which by beating pull the animal through the water.

When considering minute forms of life it is not always easy to decide which are plants and which animals. The flagellates are therefore sometimes included in botanical textbooks, because some of them use chlorophyll to make their own food just as plants do. Some textbooks, however, place these indeterminate

*Amoeba* (highly magnified)

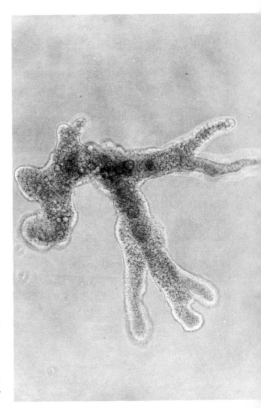

organisms – both unicellular plants and animals – in a separate kingdom, Protista.

*Euglena* is a good example of organisms of this kind. It often occurs in such numbers in ponds and ditches, or even in water butts, that a green scum forms on top of the water. Ponds or ditches receiving effluent from farm animals are good places to look for *Euglena*. Clearly this animal has chlorophyll and can therefore make its own food by photosynthesis. However, when deprived of light or living in water rich in organic food materials, some species of *Euglena* lose their green colour and begin to feed on organic nutrients in solution, absorbing them through their cell walls – a typical piece of simple animal behaviour. *Euglena* has a single flagellum at the front end of the cell and a light-sensitive area near it, and wherever possible it seems to behave like a plant.

*Ceratium*, one of the dinoflagellates, is a common member of the plankton in large lakes and floats freely in the water. One species is also found in well oxygenated ponds. It has an odd shape, with long prongs at the front and rear and two smaller ones midway. Two flagella, one large and one small, arise from the middle of the cell.

**Amoebas**  Amoebas belong to a group of the Protozoa called Rhizopoda, which means 'root-footed'. Another name for the class is Sarcodina, from two Greek words meaning 'flesh that is being rolled along', which presumably refers to the way an amoeba flows along in the water.

Several species of amoeba live in ponds and ditches, but they are not easy to see unless a quantity of bottom mud is left to settle in a glass jar for a day or two. Any amoebas that are there will be seen as tiny grey objects gliding up the sides of the jar when it is held against a dark background. With a hand-lens you will be able to see them better. Not all amoebas live in water, though. Some are common in damp soil, others among

sphagnum at the edge of ponds, and some even live in the human mouth, while amoebic dysentery is caused by a species that lives in the human large intestine.

Under a microscope a living amoeba is a somewhat disappointing object at first glance, for it is a shapeless mass of jelly-like substance – not at all like the diagrams in textbooks drawn from specimens stained to show various structures such as the nucleus and vacuoles, or spaces where food is digested. However, once the amoeba has recovered from the shock of being dropped on to a slide, it is fascinating to watch the pseudopodia, or 'false legs', streaming out from the main mass and engulfing food such as diatoms. Waste products are passed out at the surface and left behind as the animal flows on. Other vacuoles work like tiny pumps, excreting excess water and respiration takes place at the cell surface. Amoebas reproduce by the body dividing into two. When conditions are unsuitable they encyst by developing a tough coating around the cell wall and remain dormant until conditions improve. Resistant spores may develop if there is a prolonged drought or other disaster.

Not all amoebas are just naked protoplasm. *Difflugia* makes a pear-shaped shell, or 'test', from particles of sand held together with a sticky secretion. A simple 'psedopodium' emerges from the opening at the narrow end of the test to capture prey.

*Arcella* makes a dome-shaped test from a substance called chitin, similar to that in the external skeletons of insects and crustaceans. The pseudopodia are squeezed out through a central hole in the lower surface of the test. Under the microscope you can see the tests of these so-called testate rhizopods, which are common in the bottom mud of ponds rich in organic matter, looking like small yellowish-brown discs, with a central hole.

**Sun animals**  Some Pseudopodia of quite a different kind occur in a related group of

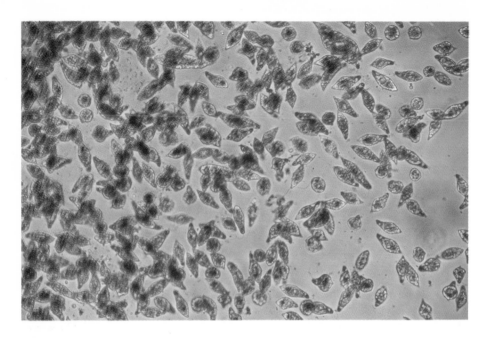

**Above** *Euglena*                    **Below** *Paramecium* in conjugation

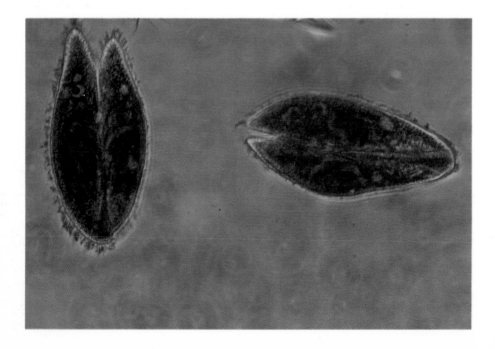

Protozoa called heliozoans or 'sun animals', for they stand out from the spherical cell of the animal like rays of the sun. They are sticky and trap minute organisms for food as the animal drifts around in the water.

**Ciliates** These, the largest group of Protozoa, are so named because they have whip-like hairs called 'cilia'. By their rhythmic beating the cilia propel the free-swimming species through the water or create currents which bring food particles to species living attached to plants or other supports.

Unlike the amoebas ciliates have a definite body shape and a gullet for taking in food. The slipper animal, *Paramecium*, is the best known ciliate and is just visible to the naked eye as a greyish speck swimming rapidly through the water. It is found in any water where there is decaying vegetable matter, such as a house gutter where wet dead leaves have collected. It also occurs, usually the second kind of organism to appear, in hay infusions. It is fascinating to watch a slipper animal under a low power of microscope as it swims rapidly in search of food, reversing if it encounters obstacles. A number will congregate around decaying vegetation where bacteria, the main food, can be gathered.

*Paramecium* reproduces by dividing into two, but at times restores vigour by reproducing sexually. Two individuals join together by their longer sides to exchange nuclear material, then separate to continue reproducing by division.

*Spirostomum* has quite a different shape from *Paramecium*. It is long and slender and more like a very small greyish worm. Sometimes whitish congregations of the animals are seen among dead leaves at the bottom of a pond. A single individual is just visible without a lens. When examined they are continually contracting into rounder shapes and then expanding again. *Spirostomum* and its relatives are interesting because they have a cell nucleus made up of a large number of smaller nuclei in

a line, which when seen under a microscope resembles a string of beads.

Stentors also have this so-called 'monoliform' nucleus. Although the various species differ in shape, most are funnel-shaped when stationary, perhaps attached to a support by their narrow end but becoming rounder when swimming about in the water. A crown of waving cilia surrounds the open end of the funnel and draws food particles into the mouth. Smaller cilia on the rest of the body propel it through the water. The largest species has a beautiful blue colour, while others are brown.

All the ciliates described so far are solitary animals. Bell animals, on the other hand, usually form social or colonial groups. In the commonest species, *Vorticella*, the individual animals, like inverted bells on long stalks, are not connected to their neighbours, each being separately attached to a support, though large numbers occur together. In *Carchesium*, however, there are many animals to a stem and each stem is connected to a main stalk. *Campanella* has the animals united to a main stalk, too. Seen in mass these ciliates resemble a fungal growth on a plant or animal to which they are attached. When disturbed the individual animals of *Vorticella* contract their

*Vorticella* (highly magnified)

stalks into a corkscrew shape and close their bells, but those in colonies are unable to do this.

Using a microscope you can see just how effective the cilia on top of the bell are, as particles are drawn to the gullet on the currents caused by their beating. You will also notice unsuitable particles being rejected just as forcibly.

At times, especially after cell division has taken place, the animals leave their stalks and become free-swimming. No doubt this is a method of dispersing the species when overcrowding occurs. In sexual reproduction two free-swimming animals conjugate.

These ciliates play an important part in our own welfare. In their method of feeding by creating currents in the water with their cilia they give out a secretion which causes small particles to clump together. This activity is taken advantage of in modern sewage treatment plants using the activated sludge system where Protozoa, especially *Vorticella* and *Campanella*, clarify the effluent and reduce it to a clear liquid that can be passed out into a stream or the sea.

Sometimes among the water plants in a pond a jelly-like mass of bell animals, often green in colour, can be seen. This is a colony of *Ophrydium* and the green colour is due to the presence of the green alga *Chlorella* in the animals' cells. This is another example of 'biological marriage'.

One ciliate that is only too well known to aquarists is the one that causes 'white spot' disease in their fish, but it also attacks coldwater fish in ponds and trout farms. It is popularly called 'ich' – pronounced 'ick' – an abbreviation of the scientific name *Ichthyophthirius multifiliis*. The first signs of infection are small white spots on the body of the fish where the ciliate has burrowed under its scales. The distressed fish try to rub off the parasites against stones or plants. After four or five days the adult parasites drop off the fish and form cysts on the bottom gravel from which up to 2,000 young ciliates emerge and swim about using their cilia in search of new fish to parasitise. The infection therefore spreads rapidly unless remedial action is taken, but solutions of methylene blue or mercurochrome are effective against the early stages.

**Sporozoans**  The animals in the last group of Protozoa are all internal parasites of other animals and have complex life histories involving two or more hosts. A typical one is *Plasmodium*, the cause of malaria in man, which after passing through several stages in the body of a mosquito is injected into a human being by the insect and goes through a series of stages in the liver, spleen, brain and blood. The cycle can be started again when the infected person is bitten by another mosquito. Until the Fens and similar breeding grounds were reduced by draining, malaria, then known as ague, was a real problem.

However, the only evidence of a sporozoan that a field naturalist is likely to find is on the body of a three-spined stickleback, where white lumps are sometimes seen on the sides of the fish. From these nodules thousands of tiny spores are released which can infect other sticklebacks. This prolific creature is named *Glugea anomala*.

# Sponges

Sponges are usually regarded as marine animals, but two species are found in fresh water: the pond sponge and the river sponge. The names are misleading. The pond sponge is more likely to be found attached to plants or other supports in slow rivers and canals, forming many finger-like growths; the river sponge occurs as flatter encrusting masses on plants, stones and submerged tree-roots in still waters. Although the natural colour of both species is greyish or yellowish, in well lighted conditions they appear green due to the presence of the green alga *Chlorella*, living symbiotically in the sponge cells.

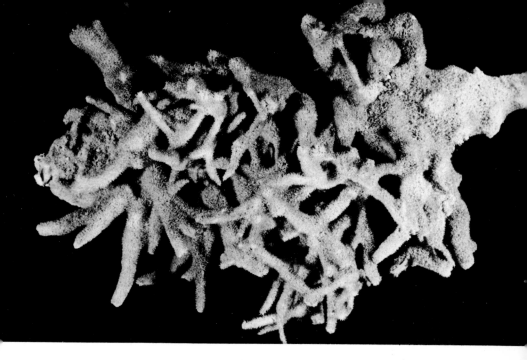

Pond sponge

The surface of sponges bears many small holes and a few larger ones – hence the scientific name of the group, Porifera or 'pore-bearers'. Through the small pores there is a constant circulation of water and, after oxygen has been extracted for respiration and any small particles of food filtered out, the water is expelled through the larger openings.

During the warm months of the year sponges increase in size by budding, but they can also reproduce sexually. Sperms are released into the water and are drawn into the current of another sponge to fertilise its eggs. From these hatch spherical larvae bearing cilia which leave the parent in its water current and, after swimming about for a day or two, settle down on some solid support and begin their development. Towards the end of summer sponges produce round gemmules, about the size of a pinhead. These are groups of cells in a tough, resistant covering. When the parent sponge dies down in winter, the gemmules fall to the bottom and remain dormant until spring, when they develop into new sponges.

Sponges give shelter to many small animals. The most interesting of these are the sponge-flies, *Sisyra*, which live on them as parasites. Freshwater sponges can sometimes block pipes and disrupt domestic water supplies.

# Coelenterates

The coelenterates (from the Greek *koilos*, hollow, and *enteron*, intestine) are another mainly marine group. Familiar examples are jellyfish, sea-anemones and corals. There is no suitable English name for them, but they are sometimes called 'hollow-bodied animals' or 'stinging animals'. In fresh water their only representatives are the hydras. These are found in both ponds and streams, attached to plants and stones.

Their structure is a step up the evolutionary ladder from sponges and has two layers of cell tissue separated by a jelly-like substance. These enclose the hollow body which acts as the food canal. Higher animals have a body

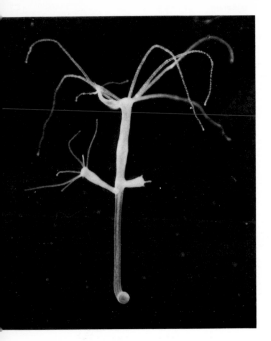

Hydra with buds

aquatic worms and even baby fish are among the prey.

Three kinds of hydra are common in this country. The green hydra is easily recognised by its colour, which is due to the presence of the alga *Chlorella*, another example of symbiosis. It usually measures about 20mm (¾ inch) in length. The brown hydra is larger – up to 25mm (1 inch) – and has long tentacles, which may be four to five times the length of the body. The slender hydra is the smallest and is only about 15mm (½ inch) long.

When disturbed, hydras contract their bodies so that they become a mere blob on a plant or stone. As a result they are not easy to see at first, but if left alone for a short time they expand first the body and then the tentacles, and their real beauty can be appreciated even under a hand lens. Under low power of a microscope they are spectacular.

In summer buds grow from the sides of

Hydra: testis near the tentacles, egg lower down the body

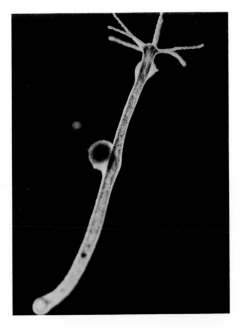

cavity, as well as a food canal, which is occupied by a variety of organs – heart, lungs, spleen and liver. This cavity is not present in coelenterates. The outer layer of the cells are specialised in their function. These include nerve cells, muscle cells, glandular cells and stinging cells. The inner layer includes cells with cilia that keep a current flowing in the hollow interior and amoeba-like cells to engulf and digest food. In hydras the only opening to the body is at the top and is surrounded by tentacles. Through this opening all food is taken in and all waste ejected, there being no anus.

The surface of the tentacles is also covered with specialised cells called cnidoblasts. These contain the harpoon-like nematocysts with which the hydra's prey is paralysed and captured. Some inject a liquid which paralyses the victim, others entangle it with fine threads. Small crustaceans such as *Daphnia*,

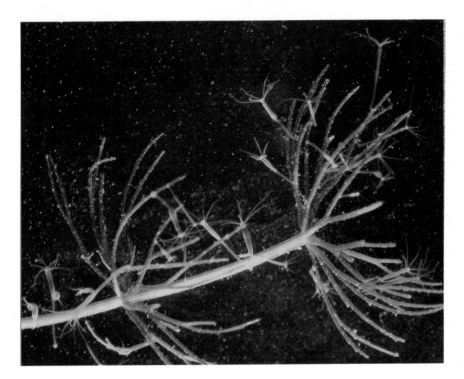

*Hydra oligactis*: many specimens on hornwort

the hydra and develop quickly into new individuals. While still attached to the parent they lead an active life, catching their own food with their tentacles; but eventually they become detached and move away. Hydras can also reproduce sexually. Each hydra is often both male and female, the male testes appearing as a small swelling near the base of the tentacles and the ovary, with a single egg, as a larger swelling further down the body. Hydras can fertilise themselves, which is unusual in the animals. The fertilised egg may stick to a plant or sink to the bottom and give rise later to a new hydra.

Hydras usually remain fixed to their support by a sticky secretion produced at the basal disc, which must be very effective as hydras can stay attached to plants in fast streams. Nevertheless, they can move about in search of food either by gliding short distances along the support or by doing a somersault –

first gripping a new hold with tentacles and mouth, then detaching the other end of the body and moving over to the new position.

A number of small animals live on hydras without apparently doing them any harm. Two ciliates, a barrel-shaped species called *Trichodina* and a flatter one resembling a small *Paramecium* and called *Kerona*, can sometimes be seen moving about the surface of a hydra removing particles of debris, bacteria and diatoms. A crustacean, *Anchistropus*, actually feeds on the outer cells of hydras, but again does not seem to injure them much. It seems strange, though, that hydras do not use their stinging cells on their visitors, which are called 'commensals'.

In some countries hydras go through an 'alternation of generations', as marine coelenterates do in their life histories. First there is a free-swimming stage called a medusa or jellyfish, which has sexual organs; then a fixed hydra-like stage, called a polyp, which reproduces by budding. The two stages are so different that it was a long time before it was realised that they were different stages of one animal and even today they often bear separate scientific names.

It caused a great sensation in 1880 when a freshwater medusa appeared in the tank in which the giant water-lily, *Victoria amazonica*, was growing in the gardens of the Royal Botanical Society in Regent's Park, London. Since then these freshwater jellyfishes, only about 12mm (½ inch) across, have appeared frequently in heated aquaria and also in canals heated by factory effluents. This medusa is named *Craspedacusta sowerbii* and it is now clear that the polyp which is called *Microhydra ryderi*, is sometimes introduced into this country on imported plants for tropical aquaria and the jellyfish stage is budded off them. *Microhydra* is only about 2mm (¹/₁₂ inch) wide and thus easily overlooked, especially as it sometimes grows singly, though colonies of up to seven polyps have been seen.

A colonial type of hydra, *Cordylophora lacustris*, is sometimes found attached to submerged parts of bridges and landing stages, usually in the slightly brackish waters of estuaries, although it can live in fresh water. The individual animals, which are pinkish in colour and have numerous tentacles, are on long branching stems. Colonies measure about 25mm (1 inch) long.

# Flatworms

The flatworms are the first animals to have that important development, a third layer of cells between the outer and inner layers. Sponges and hydras have only two layers, with an intermediate layer of jelly-like, noncellular material. It is from this third layer in higher animals that tissues and organs are made, which make them so much more efficient.

Flatworms are also the first animals displaying 'bilateral symmetry'. Simply stated, this means they have a definite head end and a left and right side which gives direction to their movements. Bilateral symmetry gives greater mobility, enabling them to pursue prey and avoid enemies more easily.

The flatworms are a large group and are divided into three classes: turbellarians, trematodes or flukes, and cestodes or tapeworms. All have both male and female organs in the same animal and are thus capable of producing both sperms and eggs. The hermaphrodites are not usually self-fertilising, except some trematodes, which live in the bodies of other animals and seldom come in contact with another of their own species.

**Turbellarians** The name comes from a Latin word which means 'a small disturbance' and refers to the water currents created by the beating of the cilia which cover the body. The very common animals called planarians are those most likely to be seen in both ponds and streams, ranging in size from about 8mm (⅓ inch) to 35mm (1⅓ inches). They are free-living animals that glide rapidly over stones or plants. They are mainly nocturnal and in the daytime should be searched for on the undersides of floating leaves or beneath stones. A bait of a small piece of meat or liver tied to a stone and left overnight in the water will have a number of planarians crawling about it in the morning, for they feed on any animal matter, dead or alive. The food is sucked up by a tube-like pharynx, which can be protruded from the underside of the animal. Aquarists should be careful not to introduce planarians to their tanks on new water plants, since they can attack both fish and their eggs.

In spring or early summer planarians lay their eggs in spherical or oval cocoons, depending on the species, and deposit them on stones or plants. There is no larval stage and small, fully formed planarians hatch from the eggs.

Identification of these small animals is based on the number of eyes and the form of the tentacles, if present. The easiest to identify is *Dendrocoelum lacteum*, because it is white in colour and large, 25mm (1 inch). It is usually found in waters with plenty of decaying vegetation where its favourite food, the water louse, is abundant. A much smaller, 12mm (½ inch), greyish planarian is *Crenobia alpina*, although its colour may vary between white and black. It has tentacles and only two eyes. It is found in small, cool streams and moves upstream in summer to find the low temperatures that are essential for its well-being. The two species of *Polycelis*, as the name implies, have many eyes around the entire edges of the front of the body. *P. nigra* is the very common black or brown planarian found in both streams and ponds, which measures about 8–10mm (¼ inch) in length. Its relative *P. felina* may be up to 25mm (1 inch) long, usually brownish-black in colour and with large pointed tentacles, which from their supposed resemblance to the ears of a cat have given it its name.

Another group of turbellarians comprises the rhabdocoeles, which are smaller than planarians and therefore often overlooked. They live mostly in still water and are usually found by examining decaying plant material from the bottom of a pond. *Dalyellia viridis* is soon picked out, as it is bright green in colour because of the presence of symbiotic algae, but others may be colourless. *Castradella* lives in the brood-pouch of the freshwater louse.

*Microstomum* feeds on hydras and manages to take the undischarged stinging cells and incorporate them into its own skin and use them for defending itself. How it does this still puzzles biologists.

**Trematodes** Better known as flukes, these flatworms are somewhat similar in their adult stages to planarians, but they are parasites for most of their life history. The name of the group comes from a Greek word meaning 'perforated' and refers to the cavity of the suckers, which somewhat resembles a perforation of the body. With the suckers they fasten themselves to their prey and suck out its body fluids.

Two types of life history are found in trematodes. In one, only a single host is attacked; but, in the other type, two, or even more, hosts are involved. The first kind are the ones most likely to be seen, as they are external parasites. These are the gill-flukes which are often found in large numbers on freshwater fish. *Gyrodactylus* is about 1mm (¹⁄₂₅ inch) in length, with a large shield-shaped disc at the rear end of its body. The mouth has glands which secrete a sticky substance around it and this no doubt helps it to hold on to its victim. *Dactylogyrus* has been known for some time in aquaria, but has now been introduced to freshwater habitats and has been found on the gills of roach. *Polystomum* is found in the adult stage in the bladder of adult frogs whilst the ciliated larvae of the parasite are found on the gills of tadpoles.

A good example of the trematodes that have more complicated life histories is the liver fluke, *Fasciola hepatica*, which causes liver-rot in sheep, cattle and many other animals, including on rare occasions human beings. The adult fluke is not an aquatic animal, but lives in the bile ducts of infected hosts. The eggs laid by it pass into sheep's intestines and thence on to the grass. Here, if the grass is damp, they hatch out into a stage called a 'miracidium', which has a coating of cilia. With these it swims until it meets a snail that lives in damp grass, usually *Lymnaea truncatula*, or the wandering snail, *L. pereger*. It bores its way into the snail and continues its development there in two stages. First it grows into a large bag-like container in which many new larvae called 'rediae' are produced. After a time these change to larvae with long

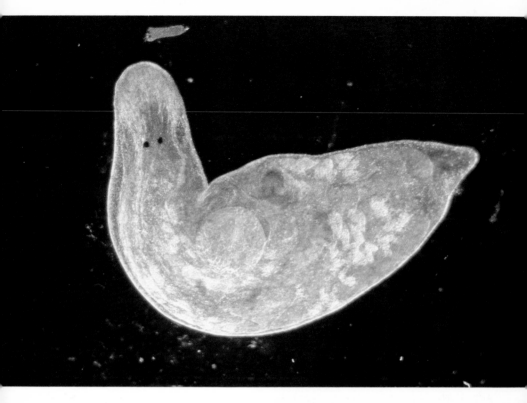

**Above** Rhabdocoele flatworm

**Right** Cercaria of liver fluke

tails called 'cercariae', which look like small tadpoles. With the aid of their tails they swim about in the water for a time, then settle on a grass stem or other support and grow a cyst around themselves. Many die at this stage, but some are swallowed by sheep or other animals feeding on the grass. The cyst breaks up in the animal's gut and the cercaria makes its way to the liver to complete the life-cycle.

It is believed that human beings can become infected by the flukes through eating watercress growing in marshy places with encysted cercaria on it. Great care should be taken to eat only watercress grown in properly supervised watercress beds, since merely

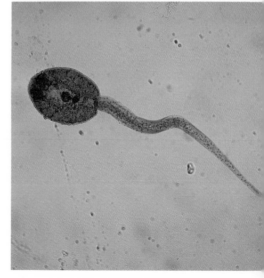

washing it in salt will not kill these parasites.

Common parasites of water birds are the schistosomes, related to the organism that causes bilharzia, which affects man in the tropics. Infection of the birds occurs when free-swimming cercaria penetrate their skin and make their way into a vein near the intestine. Human bathers in fresh water may be attacked by cercaria in mistake for birds and, as they burrow deep into the skin, they can cause a painful form of dermatitis, fairly uncommon in Britain, called 'swimmers' itch'. These parasites, too, pass their earlier stages in water snails.

Some flukes have even more complicated life-cycles. *Bucephalus* in the adult stage is a parasite of perch and pike. The miracidium stage is passed in freshwater mussels and the cercaria in one of the smaller fish such as roach. They complete their life-cycle only if the roach is eaten by a perch or pike.

*Haplometra* is found when adult in the lungs of frogs. The cercaria stage is passed in a water snail and from there it passes into the larva of a water beetle, *Ilybius*, where it encysts. Only when the beetle, in either the larval or adult stage, is eaten by a frog is the cycle completed. Here is the perfect example of a parasite adapting its life to fit in with each stage of the food chain.

**Cestodes** The final group of flatworms consists of the cestodes, or tapeworms – an appropriate name, since the adults do resemble a long piece of whitish tape. The body is partitioned off into many separate segments, each of which has its own reproductive organs, so that large numbers of eggs are produced. The body increases in length from the front end and the tail segments drop off as the eggs mature. Cestodes are parasites, the larval stage being passed in one species and the adult in another animal which eats the first. The head, or scolex, of an adult tapeworm has suckers and sometimes hooks, both of which help it hold on to the wall of the host's food canal. Food digested by the host animal is thus absorbed through the body surface of the parasite.

*Schistocephalus gasterostei* may be taken as an example of the life history of a tapeworm. The adult lives in the digestive tract of fish-eating birds, such as the kingfisher and heron. The eggs, when ready for hatching, are passed out in bird's droppings. The ciliated larvae which emerge swim around until they encounter a small crustacean such as *Cyclops*, where they undergo further development and in time form a cyst. Their future survival depends on the *Cyclops* being eaten by a fish, such as a stickleback, when the cyst breaks open. The larva becomes active again and grows into a stage so large that it causes a bulge under the gill-covers of the fish. Finally, to complete the cycle, the fish must be eaten by a bird, and the parasite then changes into an adult tapeworm.

# Roundworms

Roundworms, threadworms, or nematodes (from the Greek, meaning 'thread-like') are abundant both on land and in water. Some, for example eelworms, are important as agricultural pests; others cause diseases such as hookworm in man and in his domestic animals.

Not all are parasites, however, and it is the free-living species that are encountered in pond-hunting, for they frequently appear when debris from the bottom of a pond is examined under a microscope. *Dorylaimus*, one of the largest, is about 6mm (¼ inch) in length but another common one, *Rhabdolaimus*, is only about 1mm (¹/₂₅ inch) long.

The body of a roundworm is thread-like and has no cilia, and they move through the water by vigorous whip-like movements, contracting the body into S-shaped curves. Through the transparent skin the food canal can be observed running almost the entire length of the body. However, no breathing organs can be seen – the animal absorbs the oxygen it needs through its skin. The food of free-swimming roundworms varies from species to species. *Dorylaimus* feeds on small animals and its mouth has a 'stylet' for sucking out their body fluids. Others feed on the remains of dead plants and animals and are useful pond cleaners.

Little is known of the part roundworms play in the economy of fresh waters but, judging by the numbers that live there, it is probably an important one. Here is a good example of work which could be done by a dedicated amateur naturalist.

## Hairworms

Much larger than the roundworms are the strange animals called hairworms – they can grow as long as 60cm (2 feet) and are well named, since they do look like horsehairs. As they can appear suddenly in drinking troughs and other small receptacles around a farm, it is little wonder that in days gone by they were thought to be horsehairs that had come to life.

Their life history seems equally strange. From eggs laid in long strings, usually on water plants, hatch many larvae that swim about in the water, then encyst on waterside vegetation. To continue their life-cycle the larvae must, in some way that is not quite clear, gain access to suitable insects – such as grasshoppers, crickets, and both land and water beetles. They bore through the wall of the gut and live as parasites. A long proboscis armed with stylets enables the tiny larva, which themselves are only about a millimetre long, to carry out this penetration.

After several months, usually in spring or early summer, adult hairworms emerge from their hosts. It is believed that if the latter are land insects, they seek water when this emergence is about to happen, since the newly emerged worms soon die if they do not reach water. Great masses of hairworms may be found at the time of emergence seemingly tangled inseparably in a 'Gordian knot' – hence the scientific name of *Gordius* which has

Hairworm

been given to them. After pairing and egg-laying the adult hairworms soon die.

## Proboscis roundworms

Parasitic animals thought to be related to the roundworms are the Acanthocephala, or proboscis roundworms. The adults have a stout proboscis armed with hooks at the front end of the body used to bore into the food canal of the host animal in which they live. The scientific name of the group means 'thorn-headed', in reference to this proboscis.

The early stages of these animals live as parasites in crustaceans and in the larvae of insects. The adults are usually found in fresh-water fish, including pike, perch, minnow and trout.

The orange-coloured early stage of *Polymorphus minutus* can sometimes be seen in the body cavity of the freshwater shrimp,

*Gammarus*, and that of *Acanthocephalus clavula* in the water louse, *Asellus*. The parasite completes its development into an adult when these crustaceans are eaten by fish.

# True worms

The true worms, or annelids, are at a much higher stage of development than the worm-like animals described in the last few pages. The word 'annelid' is derived from a French word meaning 'arranged in rings'; examination of the body of a typical member of the group, a garden earthworm, will show how appropriate a description this is. The rings mark off the body into obvious segments and an earthworm has about a hundred and fifty of them. Annelids are hermaphrodites but cross-fertilisation is necessary, and the sperm of one worm must fertilise the eggs of another. Eggs are enclosed in a cocoon which is formed by the 'clitellum', a swollen structure near the head end of the worm. Starting as a kind of collar encircling the body, it is later passed over the head and the ends close to form a capsule, which is either deposited on a support or in aquatic species merely dropped to the bottom of the water.

Anyone who has watched a bird tugging at a worm on a lawn will have noticed how difficult it is to dislodge the worm. This is because of the strong bristles that arise from each segment and can hold fast to the sides of the burrow in the soil. By means of these bristles worms can take a grip on the ground when crawling about. Not all annelids have bristles, though, so they serve as a simple way of dividing the animals into three main groups: the polychaetes ('many bristles'), most of which are marine and will not be mentioned here; the oligochaetes ('few bristles'); and the leeches, which have no bristles.

**Oligochaetes** These are common in all freshwater habitats and some could be mis-taken for land worms that have strayed into the water. This is the case with the square-tailed worm, *Eiseniella*, which is found in the mud either at the water's edge or on land. It is about 50mm (2 inches) long and can readily be identified by its square-shaped rear end.

*Lumbriculus* is another species similar to the earthworm, although it belongs to a different family and is truly aquatic. It may reach a length of 75mm (3 inches) and is found both in still water and in slow-moving streams. This worm can divide into several smaller individuals.

Members of the family Naididae habitually divide in this way, yet remain joined so that chains of several individuals are often seen, but because they are small they are usually overlooked. An exception is *Chaetogaster diaphanus*, which is about 25mm (1 inch) long but quite transparent and so needs looking for carefully. *Chaetogaster limnaei*, 7mm (¼ inch) lives attached to water snails or in the burrows of the bloodworm larva of the midge *Chironomus*.

*Stylaria*, 15mm (½ inch), can easily be identified by the very long thin proboscis at the front end of the body.

A patch of mud with many small holes at the edge of a pond or stream gives away the site of a colony of river worms, *Tubifex*, a worm much in demand by aquarists for feeding their fish. Wait a little time and a multitude of small waving pink tails will emerge from the holes. Their owners are buried head down in little tunnels, passing mud through their bodies to extract the particles of detritus on which they feed. An incautious footstep makes them vanish instantly by retreating into their burrows. The worms have in their blood a high concentration of the red pigment hemo-globin, which absorbs oxygen; they can exist in heavily polluted waters too deficient in oxygen for most freshwater animals.

White worms, up to 25mm (1 inch) long, living among the roots of water plants and resembling the roots themselves, are pot-worms, members of the large family Enchytraeidae, of which 40 species are found in Britain, some seeming as much at home on land as in water.

As on land, all these worms serve a useful purpose in the water as scavengers, as well as providing an abundant food supply for other animals.

**Leeches** Leeches can always be distinguished from the other worms in water by their suckers, a small one at the head end surrounding the mouth, not always easy to see, and a much larger one at the rear end of the body. The large sucker enables the leech to attach itself either to its prey or to a stone or other support when it is resting after gorging itself with a meal. The small sucker is, of course, used to hold the victim to allow the jaws, or the proboscis in those leeches that have no jaws, to perform this bloodthirsty task, for most leeches feed on the blood of other animals.

The only leech in Britain that can penetrate the human skin is the medicinal leech, which is now rare. It is about 85mm (3¼ inches) long and is usually identified by reddish stripes running the length of the otherwise olive-green body. It is still found in some traditional habitats where horses and cattle come to drink, on which the leech can prey. Suitable sites are still found in the Lake District, the New Forest, Anglesey, South Wales and the western areas of Scotland. It was always believed that the medicinal leech needed mammalian blood if it was to breed, but doubt is now thrown on this belief and leeches certainly seem to thrive in ponds where no horses or cattle visit, presumably living on blood from toads, frogs and small fish.

The native supply dwindled in the early part of the nineteenth century, when leeches were in great demand for curing a variety of illnesses. Nearly 57½ million leeches were

Medicinal leech: underside to show the suckers

said to be imported from France in the year 1832 alone and leech farms existed there until recent times. There has lately been a revival in the medical uses of leeches and in 1982 they were reintroduced to the National Health Service for sucking clotted blood after microsurgery and following eye operations.

The slightly smaller 'horse leech' is found in ponds and streams and it leaves the water more readily than other leeches in search of food, also when depositing its egg-cocoon under stones or among grass roots. The name is probably a case of mistaken identity. As it was often found around the edges of ponds where horses drank, it was assumed that it was the one that attached itself to the animals and sucked their blood. Its background colouring is often similar to the medicinal leech's, but it lacks the reddish stripes.

However, the horse leech does not suck blood at all but swallows prey whole if they are small, and seems partial to earthworms, tadpoles, insects and young fish. It has been seen eating a toad, which presumably had died.

**Above** Medicinal leech

**Below** *Theromyzon tessulatum*, with young attached to the underside

Both the horse leech and the medicinal leech have jaws; but of the sixteen species of leech known to live in Britain nine have a proboscis instead of jaws with which to penetrate the tissues of their prey, and five species have neither jaws nor proboscis.

In the second group is the fish parasite *Piscicola geometra*, a very distinctive leech with a slim body with large well defined suckers. Its victims include trout, salmon, bream, perch, pike, sticklebacks, gudgeon and stone loach. It needs well oxygenated waters and is usually found in fast streams and rivers or in the margins of lakes. It attaches itself to the mouth, gills or other parts of the body of its host.

A parasite of water birds is *Theromyzon tessulatum*, which enters the nostrils and throat of ducks, geese and swans to suck their blood. When satiated, it falls from its prey and hides under stones. Eggs are laid in June or July in cocoons at the bottom of the water and the female covers them with her body. When the young hatch, they attach themselves to the underside of the female and are carried about by her in groups of up to 300 for three or four months.

*Theromyzon* is found in ponds and lake margins, but not in fast streams like the last species.

# Rotifers

Rotifers (Latin *rota*, a wheel; *fero*, to bear) are all very small animals and a microscope is needed to examine them. Ever since they were first discovered in 1687 by the Dutch microscopist Antoni van Leeuwenhoek, naturalists have been fascinated by their diversity of form, mode of life and sheer beauty. Some are even smaller than Protozoa, but their many-celled bodies have a much more complex internal structure, with reproductive, nervous and excretory systems. They are almost exclusively freshwater animals, only a few species occurring in the sea.

The feature that gives the group its name is the crown of cilia at the head end of the body, which, when in action, creates the illusion of rotating wheels. The rhythmic beating of the cilia serves the dual purpose of propelling the free-swimming species through the water and bringing food particles to the mouth. Not all rotifers are free-swimming, though. Some remain attached to plants by means of a sticky secretion produced from glands at the rear end of the body; others, the so-called bdelloid rotifers (Latin *bdella*, a leech), creep about like leeches or looper caterpillars, first securing the front end to a support, then arching the body and bringing the rear end to the front. A few live as parasites on other animals.

The mouth in all rotifers leads to a 'mastax', an organ unique to this group of animals. It consists of a pair of strong jaws which break down the food before it passes to the stomach for digestion. The structure of the mastax is the main feature used to separate families of rotifers.

Although they have a well developed digestive system rotifers have no blood or special breathing organs, so they carry out respiration through their skin. Eyes, reddish in colour, occur in many species, either singly or as a pair. Most rotifers seen are females and in some species males have never been observed, but when they occur they are smaller than the females and incapable of feeding, so they soon die. The females can produce two kinds of eggs without fertilisation. Small ones develop into males and large ones into females. A resting egg can also be produced, which can survive unfavourable conditions and develop later when things have returned to normal. Some rotifers can form a cyst when droughts occur.

The reddish sediment found in bird-baths mentioned on page 32 often contains the cysts of a common rotifer, *Philodina roseola*. If a little is scraped off and left in water, the active rotifer will soon be seen moving about. This is a member of the bdelloid rotifers. A related species lives on polyzoans (page 54). *Embata*

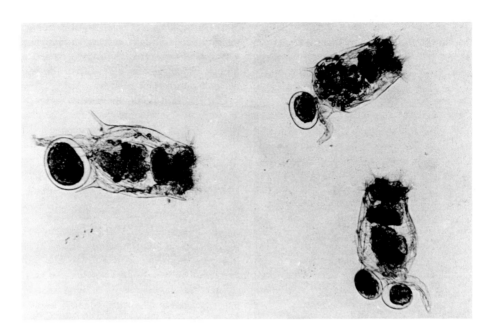

*parasitica*, another bdelloid, is found attached to the freshwater shrimp and freshwater louse.

Perhaps the best known of the free-swimming rotifers are the many species of *Brachionus*, shaped like a wine-glass without a base. The females carry their eggs attached to the rear of their bodies until the young hatch.

*Floscularia ringens* is one of the rotifers that live attached to water plants. It makes a cylindrical case built up, brick by brick, from particles abstracted from the water and cemented together with the animal's own waste products. When alarmed, it withdraws into the case; but when it is feeding the four lobes of the crown of cilia protrude from the top of the case. *Limnias ceratophylli* makes a similar case, though smaller and made from a horny secretion of the body. *Conochilus* forms colonies of many individuals which swim freely through the water. They are about 1mm ($\frac{1}{25}$ inch) across.

Even more beautiful are two species in which the body is enclosed in a wide trans-

**Above** Rotifers, *Brachionus* with eggs (highly magnified)

**Below** Rotifier, *Philodina* (highly magnified)

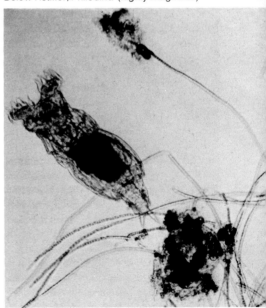

parent sheath, not always easy to see. *Collotheca campanulata* is funnel-shaped with five large protuberances around the rim, each of which bears many very long cilia. These do not beat, but form a funnel directing prey into the mouth.

*Stephanoceros* has a corona which is drawn out into five long, pointed arms, which curve inwards and have whorls of cilia on their inner sides. These draw floating particles towards the mouth. *Stephanoceros* is, indeed, a most beautiful object to watch under a microscope, especially under dark ground illumination.

Rotifer, *Stephanoceros fimbriatus* (highly magnified)

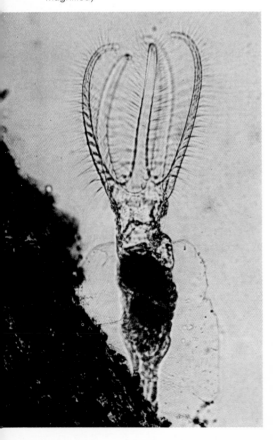

# Gastrotrichs

These are very small animals, none larger than about 1·5mm ($^1/_{20}$ inch). Although often overlooked, they are commonly to be found in the debris at the bottom of ponds and ditches. They feed on even smaller bacteria, algae, protozoans and organic debris. They are roughly cylindrical in shape with a definite head end where the mouth is situated, and a forked tail.

The name gastrotrich (Greek *gastr-*, stomach; *trich*, hair) and the usual common names 'hairy-back' and 'bristle-back' refer to the bristles arising from scales on the back of most familiar species. Cilia on the underside of the body enable the animals to move about over surfaces or swim freely in the water. Some can even jump by jerking their movable spines.

All freshwater gastrotrichs are hermaphrodite. Two types of eggs are laid: those that hatch almost immediately, and others which can survive adverse conditions and hatch only when things improve.

The larger species of the genus *Chaetonotus* (of which sixteen species are known in Britain) are those you will most generally notice when examining pond debris under a microscope.

# Moss animals

The animals in this group are mainly marine, only nine species occurring in fresh water. They live in colonies often composed of many individuals joined in a jelly-like mass, a feature from which one of the scientific names given to them, Polyzoa (Greek *poly*, many; *zoon*, an animal), is derived. Usually the colonies are found attached to submerged plants or other objects and resemble clumps of moss, which has given rise to another scientific name, Bryozoa (moss animals). A third more recent name, Ectoprocta, refers to an anatomical feature: the fact that the anus opens outside the lophophore, which is the crowning glory of moss animals. This is a kind of platform

bearing a flower-like crest of waving tentacles covered with hair-like cilia. With these the animals create a whirlpool in the water around them which drives food to the mouth, situated at the base of the tentacles. The tentacles are withdrawn instantly if danger threatens, making moss animals difficult to find. Close examination, preferably in late summer, of the undersides of water-lily leaves, submerged tree-roots and particularly wooden posts of jetties, bridges and landing stages in canals or 'lakes' in public parks will often reveal jelly-like masses of moss animals. Places where there is a gentle circulation of water seem to be especially good sites for finding the animals.

Some species, including *Cristatella*, soon expand their tentacles; but others, such as the common species *Plumatella*, may take up to an hour to do so. The size of the colonies varies greatly with the species. Those of *Plumatella* may measure several metres across, but the elongated colonies of *Cristatella* are rarely more than 100mm (4 inches) long and those of *Lophopus* about 500mm (20 inches) across. *Cristatella* occasionally creeps about slowly as a colony. How this is achieved is not known, but presumably the individual animals react in a unified way to external stimuli such as light or temperature.

Reproduction is carried out both sexually and asexually. The individual animals are hermaphrodite and can produce both eggs and sperms, from the union of which ciliated embryos develop and swim away. At times of active growth buds are also produced, while in autumn overwintering bodies called 'statoblasts' are formed within the individual animals and are released when the colonies disintegrate in the winter. Statoblasts can survive for several years and are resistant to freezing and drought. Sometimes they can be found in floating debris at the edge of ponds. In this way they may be transported on the plumage of birds or animal fur to other ponds and start new colonies there.

# Molluscs

Molluscs include snails, slugs, mussels, cuttle-fish and octopuses. Their origins were in the sea, but some, perhaps by way of estuaries, became adapted to living in the fresh waters of rivers and lakes, and later colonised the land. Surprisingly, some of the latter returned to the water, so we now have in our ponds and streams both species truly adapted to living in water, which breathe oxygen dissolved in the water, and others only secondarily aquatic, which still need to breathe atmospheric air.

The body of a mollusc is soft, as implied in the name (Latin *molluscus*, soft), and is not divided into segments. In snails and mussels a hard shell protects the body, of which it is an integral part, not merely a loose case in which to live. The shell is secreted in liquid form by a fold in the body wall, called the mantle, and is added to at its edges as the animal grows. It is easy to see the lines of growth on the edges of a mussel shell. In snails the shell is really a tube twisted into a number of whorls, new and larger whorls being produced as the snail grows.

The shell is a more complex structure than it seems. It consists of three distinct layers: a thin, skin-like outer layer made from a material similar to the outer surface of insects; the thicker, main layer which is very hard; and an inner layer of mother-of-pearl. The last two consist largely of calcium carbonate (lime), which explains why generally molluscs prefer to live in 'hard' waters. They need lime for their shells, but this substance also makes particles of clay lump together and fall to the bottom, leaving the water clear. Lime salts, too, are good for the growth of plants and so help provide a rich food supply for the molluscs.

Freshwater molluscs are divided into two classes: gastropods, which include snails and limpets; and bivalves, comprising mussels and orb-shell and pea-shell cockles.

**Gastropods** The word gastropod (derived from two Greek words, *gaster*, belly; and *podos*, foot) refers to the large muscular development of the lower side of the body called the foot. It is the sole on which a snail moves about and its undersurface can be seen in action if you watch a water snail climbing up the glass front of an aquarium. Near the head end is a small opening through which a kind of tongue called a 'radula', bearing many rows of teeth, is protruded to scrape off the algae or other plant material on which it feeds.

If the specimen being observed is one of the species of *Lymnaea*, such as the great pond snail, *L. stagnalis*, you will notice another larger opening when the snail reaches the surface of the water. This is a breathing tube through which it takes in atmospheric air for respiration. The opening communicates with the lung, situated between the mantle and the rear wall of the body, which gives this group of air-breathing snails the name Pulmonata, from the Latin word for a lung. Clearly, these are snails that returned to the water late in their evolution.

The large shell of the great pond snail needs a lot of calcium carbonate, so this species can thrive only in waters containing plenty of lime. The eggs are laid in long, sausage-shaped gelatinous masses attached to plants or stones.

In contrast, a commoner species, the wandering snail *L. peregra*, seems able to manage with minimum quantities of calcium, for it is found in all kinds of fresh water and even occurs in brackish water. *L. truncatula*, an even smaller species with a shell height of only about 8mm (⅓ inch), is the usual inter-mediate host of the liver fluke. It lives in marshy pastures and at the edges of ditches and small streams.

The shell of the ramshorn snail is coiled in a flat spiral and ranges in size from the largest species, the great ramshorn, *Planorbarius corneus*, over 25mm (1 inch) across, to the tiny nautilus ramshorn, *P. crista*, less than 3mm (⅛ inch) across. The eggs are laid in flat roughly circular masses on any suitable support.

Ramshorn snails have in their blood the red pigment haemoglobin. These snails are therefore better adapted to living in water than most pulmonates and need to rise to the surface less frequently – and in well oxygenated waters hardly at all. The lovely red ramshorn, an albino variety of the great ramshorn popular with aquarists, lacks the normal brown colouring in the shell and body so that the red blood shows through.

The river limpet has quite a different kind of shell from the snails. It is conical in shape, without whorls. In spite of its name, the river limpet lives also in ponds, streams and lakes, firmly fixed to stones. It is about 5mm (⅕ inch) high and 6mm (¼ inch) across. The lake limpet is smaller and not so common.

Better adapted to living in water, because they have gills for extracting oxygen, are the primarily aquatic snails now known as Prosobranchia (Greek *proso*, forward; *branchia*, gills). These were formerly called operculates – a more useful name, because attached to their foot they have a horny or chalky plate called an 'operculum' with which they can close the opening of the shell when they withdraw into it. This is a much more solid covering than the mucus with which some land snails close the entrance to their shells during dry periods or in hibernation.

The best known operculates are freshwater winkles, or river snails, *Viviparus viviparus* and *V. fasciatus*, which live in slow-moving waters as far north as Yorkshire. The latter species also occurs in still waters. Their shells are rounder than those of pond snails, about 35mm (1⅓ inches) high and brownish in general colouring, with darker spiral bands round the whorls. The female has long tapering tentacles, but the male has the right-hand tentacle short and blunt. As the scientific name implies, these snails are viviparous, the eggs being retained in the female's body until the young are fully formed.

Jenkins' spire shell, *Potamopyrgus jenkinsi*, which is only about 5mm (⅕ inch) high, is interesting as it has colonised fresh water only in recent times. Until 1893 it was known only in brackish water, but it has now spread to fresh water over most of Britain, favouring running water rather than still.

**Bivalves** In bivalves, as the name implies, the shell is in two parts, or valves, hinged together by an elastic ligament. The swan mussel, *Anodonta cygnea*, is the best known species. Its oval shell, usually about 135mm long by 70mm high (5½ × 2¾ inches),

Swan mussel: inhalent siphon to the left, exhalent siphon to the right

Glochidia larvae of swan mussel

**Above** Great pond snails

**Left** Great ramshorn snails

**Below** Freshwater winkle (male)

although it may measure up to 230mm (9 inches), is found in large ponds, canals and slow rivers, embedded at an angle in the mud and securely anchored by its foot. When it is feeding, the two parts of the shell are opened slightly and two small tubes protrude from the rear end. The lower one is larger and is called the inhalent siphon, and through it a constant current of water is drawn into the shell and passes over the mantle cavity, where oxygen is extracted for respiration by gills, and floating particles of food are filtered out. The water is then expelled by the upper, smaller exhalent siphon. Beating cilia on the gills keep the water circulating.

There are both male and female mussels and in summer sperm from the males is released into the water and taken into the female's inhalent siphon to fertilise the eggs, but the resulting young do not complete their development until the following spring. The young, which are called glochidia larvae, leave their parent through her exhalent siphon. They have small bivalve shells bearing sharp teeth on the ends of the valves and a sticky thread, called a byssus, projecting from the shell. After swimming about for a time by opening and closing their shells they eventually become attached by their byssus to water plants, where their future development depends on a fish passing near enough to become attached to the byssus and carry off the larva. This embeds itself with its sharp teeth into the skin of the fish and remains there as a parasite, sucking its blood. After about three months the glochidia leave their hosts, drop to the bottom of the water and lead a normal existence.

The duck mussel, *Anodonta anatina*, is slightly smaller, more oval and fatter than the swan mussel. It is found in similar habitats. The painter's mussel, *Unio pictorum*, is a smaller species, so-named because the early Dutch painters used the valves of the shell for holding their paints; also, gold leaf and silver leaf used by artists in illuminating manuscripts were in more recent times sold in the shells. The pearl mussel, *Margaritifera margaritifera*, lives in fast streams in the north of Britain and in Ireland, and there were commercial pearl fisheries on the river Tay in Perthshire for many years. It is thought that the pearl is usually formed around the larva of a fluke or tapeworm, the adult stage of which is passed in a water bird. Its presence in the delicate tissue of the mussel causes the mollusc to surround it with layers of nacre, the pearl-making substance.

Orb-shell cockles are much smaller than mussels. The largest species, the horny orb-shell, *Sphaerium corneum*, has a regular, rounded shell about 11mm (nearly ½ inch) long and is found at the bottom of most kinds of freshwater habitats.

Pea-shell cockles are even smaller, with shells ranging in size from 7mm (¼ inch) to 1·5mm (¹/₂₀ inch), which are more convex and are irregularly shaped. They are common in all kinds of freshwater habitats and are found in the sand or mud at the bottom.

## Arthropods

The arthropods (Greek *arthron*, a joint; *podos*, a foot), or jointed-limbed animals, are the largest division of the animal kingdom and include such well-known examples as crabs, lobsters, shrimps, crayfish, water fleas, insects, spiders, mites, centipedes and millipedes. Most live in the sea; nevertheless, three-quarters of the animals living in fresh waters are arthropods. It is possible here only to mention a few representatives.

The feature after which the arthropods are named, the paired jointed-limbs or appendages, have specialised functions such as walking, swimming, capturing prey and even breathing. All arthropods have a skin covered with a tough cuticle made from chitin, which is often strengthened with deposits of lime. Since this outer covering or shell gives structural strength and anchorage for the muscles, it is in effect an external skeleton. Because

it cannot stretch, it has to be moulted at intervals as the animal grows, leaving the animal unprotected and vulnerable. In the course of their development most arthropods undergo a metamorphosis with a larval stage that is often quite unlike the adult.

## Crustaceans

As crustaceans (Latin *crusta*, a shell) are primarily aquatic animals, they breathe oxygen dissolved in the water either through gills or, in smaller species, through their whole body surface.

The branchiopods, or gill-footed crustaceans, are so called because they have flat swimming appendages that also act as gills. The fairy shrimps, *Chirocephalus diaphanus*, are beautiful and interesting animals about 25mm (1 inch) long. They live in small pools which dry out in the summer, and so are usually to be seen only for short periods of the year. They swim actively with rapid beating of their swimming appendages, at the same time filtering out the microscopic organisms on which they feed and keeping a constant circulation of water to bring fresh supplies of oxygen to their gills. The usual position for swimming is upside down, but occasionally fairy shrimps turn over to stir up food from the bottom of the pool.

Fairy shrimp: **left**, nauplius larva; **right**, adult

Eggs laid by the female sink to the bottom mud. When the pool dries up, they remain dormant until it fills with water again. The young which then hatch are unlike their parents and are called nauplius larvae.

Another inhabitant of temporary pools is apus, *Triops cancriformis*, now very rare in Britain. It is larger than the fairy shrimp and has a large shield-like shell somewhat resembling that of a crab.

The familiar water fleas exist in immense numbers in the plankton of still waters, providing abundant food for many of the larger animals. The many species of *Daphnia* are perhaps the best known. When examined under a microscope, they are seen to have a shell all in one piece, but folded over the back, resembling a bivalve mollusc. The whole internal structure can be seen through the transparent shell – including the food canal, through which the passage of microscopic plants which the animal has eaten can be studied, the eggs in the brood-chamber, and even the beating of the heart. The large compound eye made up of many facets and the muscles controlling it are equally fascinating. *Daphnia* keeps its place in the water by vigorous strokes of the second pair of antennae which propel it in a series of upward jerks – hence its common name, because of the resemblance to the jumps of true fleas, although, of course, they are not related.

Food is strained out of the water passing through the shell by bristles on the legs and is then passed to the mouth. In summer only females occur, which lay eggs that do not need fertilisation. These are kept in the brood-pouch on the back of the animal until the young hatch, usually only a day or two after laying. In a few days they make their way into the water. When winter or other unfavourable conditions approach, some of the eggs hatch into males. These fertilise the females and then larger, fertilised eggs appear in a special thick-walled compartment called an 'ephippium'. Only two or three of these 'winter eggs' are laid. On the death of the parent the eggs, still in their ephippium, either float in the water or sink to the bottom, depending on the species of water flea. When favourable conditions return these hatch into small water fleas. It is probable that these winter eggs get carried from pond to pond in mud on birds' feet, for water fleas can suddenly appear in newly made ponds.

Water fleas have haemoglobin in their blood and when the oxygen level of the water becomes depleted they can increase the amount of haemoglobin to such an extent that they appear red and colour the water when they are present in large numbers.

Another group of small crustaceans particularly abundant in weedy ponds are the ostracods, of which the genus *Cypria* is the best known. They feed mainly on decaying material at the bottom of the pond, but are often to be seen scuttling rapidly through the water. When disturbed they withdraw their antennae and pair of slender legs, the only parts that are ever extended from the shell, and drop to the bottom of the water. The shell is very distinctive, shaped like a bean and sometimes green in colour, although brown or yellow specimens are more usual. They

measure only about 1·5mm ($^{1}/_{16}$ inch) long.

Copepods are another large group of crustaceans with both free-living and parasitic members. The many species of *Cyclops* are familiar to all pond-hunters as they occur in all kinds of habitats, but the largest is only about 4mm ($^{1}/_{6}$ inch) long. The body of a *Cyclops* is pear-shaped with two long tail appendages. The underside of the body, which is always the hardest to see, carries numerous pairs of limbs, some for swimming and others for seizing food. On the head is the single eye from which the name has been given in allusion to the giants of Greek mythology. The food varies with the species. Some capture living prey such as worms, fly larvae and even other small crustaceans, but others feed on plant material.

It is the female *Cyclops* that attracts attention, for attached to the rear of her body are two large bags of eggs. From these eggs hatch nauplius larvae which develop into adults in three to four weeks after several · moults. No resting eggs are known in species of *Cyclops*. The male *Cyclops* is somewhat smaller than the female and has larger antennae, in some species modified for grasping the female during mating.

The colours of adult *Cyclops* vary with the species; some are almost colourless, while others are blue, green or reddish. The abundance of these crustaceans in freshwater habitats makes them important items in the food of other animals. Some are intermediate hosts of the tapeworm parasite of water birds, *Schistocephalus*, mentioned in the section on flatworms (page 47).

Some members of the Cyclopoida are external parasites of fish. Several species of *Ergasilus* live on the gills of a variety of freshwater fish. *Thersitina* attacks sticklebacks, both three-spined and ten-spined, and attaches itself to the gill area. *Lernaea*, or the anchorworm, has been found on fish of the carp family, whilst *Salminicola*, the gill maggot, confines its activities to the salmon. Also found on salmon

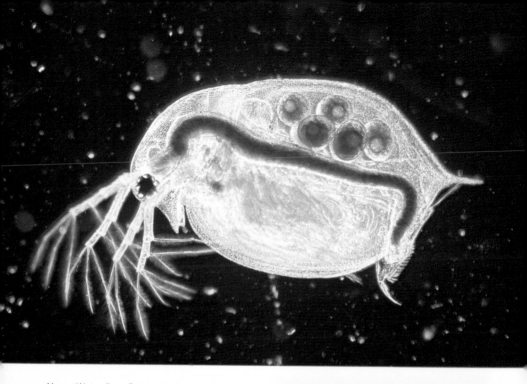

**Above** Water flea, *Daphnia pulex*

**Below** Ostracod, *Ilyodromus olivaceus*

**Right** *Cyclops*: female with egg-sacs

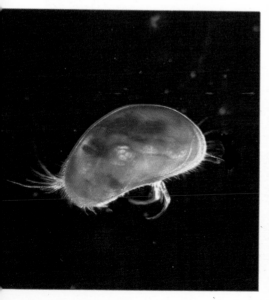

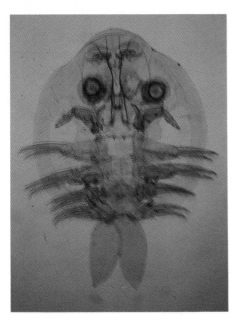

is a marine copepod, the so-called sea-louse, *Lepeophtheirus*, which remains on the fish after they have returned from the sea to breed in fresh water, but soon dies. Fishermen learn to recognise the sea-louse, which tells them that their catch is fresh from the sea.

Unfortunately, the great increase in the importation of fish from other countries and their wide distribution here have resulted in the appearance of eight species of fish parasites new to Britain in recent years, and no doubt the trend will continue.

Fish lice belong to a different group of crustaceans, Branchiura. They are not, of course, true lice – for lice are insects – but their manner of attaching themselves to their host and sucking its blood is similar. Only one

**Left** Fish louse, *Argulus coregoni*

**Below** Freshwater crayfish

genus, *Argulus*, occurs in Britain and *A. folia-ceus* is the commonest species. It is about 8mm (⅓ inch) long with a very flattened leaf-like body, the most noticeable features of which are the huge suckers on the underside of the body. The combination of the flattened body and the suckers ensures that *Argulus* can remain firmly attached to its host even in rapidly flowing waters. Between the suckers is a hollow spine, which is repeatedly inserted into the skin of the fish and possibly injects either a liquid to prevent the blood from clotting or a narcotic to quieten the victim. Blood is not the only substance that is taken, and the powerful jaws rasp off the tissues of the fish and no doubt mucus and skin are sucked up by the mouth as well.

In late summer the female *Argulus* lays its clumps of eggs, up to 200 to a clutch, covered with a gelatinous envelope, on stones or other supports. The larvae hatch in about a month and attach themselves to fish, but they undergo several moults before they are adult.

The larger freshwater crustaceans are included in a major subdivision called Malacostraca (Greek *malakos*, soft; *ostrakon*, a shell). Only three groups need concern us

Freshwater shrimp, *Gammarus*

here, for the others are unlikely to be seen in ponds and streams.

The familiar water louse, *Asellus*, which is about 20mm (¾ inch) long when adult, is found in all weedy ponds and streams, usually among the debris at the bottom on which it feeds. It resembles the woodlice that crowd together under logs and stones in our gardens. In spring the female carries her mass of white eggs on the underside of her body. The young resemble their mother when they hatch and they remain attached to her for a time.

The freshwater shrimp, *Gammarus* (which is not a close relative of the seaside shrimps), is also common in streams, ditches and ponds, usually where there is at least a slight flow of water. Its body, about 25–30mm (1–1⅕ inches), is flattened from side to side and its habit of lying or moving on its side enables it to squeeze under stones and survive even in fast streams. In spring and summer two shrimps will often be seen swimming in tandem, the larger male on the back of the female. The fertilised eggs are carried by her in a brood-pouch under the front part of her body and the young, which resemble the parents, remain there for a few days after hatching.

Like the water louse, the freshwater shrimp is a scavenger with a particular liking for decaying leaves that have blown into the water from the land. Both crustaceans are important converters of plant material into a form suitable for fish and other animals.

The largest of all freshwater crustaceans is the freshwater crayfish, now with the formidable scientific name of *Austropotamobius pallipes* after several name changes in recent years. It resembles a small lobster, but its average length is only about 100mm (4 inches), although larger specimens sometimes occur. The males are larger than the females.

Crayfish are found only in well oxygenated waters and thrive best in the 'hard' water of streams and rivers in limestone or chalk districts, where there are sufficient calcium salts to make their comparatively large shells, which are moulted at intervals. They feed on any small prey they can catch with their powerful pincer-like front claws, including water snails, insect larvae and possibly small fish.

Pairing takes place in the autumn. The male turns the female onto her back and releases seminal fluid, which sticks to her abdomen. Hidden away in a burrow in the bank of the stream, she lays about a hundred pink eggs and attaches them to her swimmerets, the four pairs of appendages on her abdomen which assist her in swimming, where they come into contact with the male sperm and are fertilised. The eggs do not hatch until spring and remain attached to her. In this condition she is said to be 'in berry'. When the young hatch, they stay with the parent for a time but eventually drop off to lead an independent existence.

The freshwater crayfish is very sensitive to pollution and is, therefore, now in a very vulnerable position in many areas.

## Insects

Insects are the most adaptable and successful animals that have evolved. Indeed, there are few places where they are not found. They can exist in such unlikely habitats as hot springs and glaciers; they range from the summits of mountains to the sea shore and from tundra to the tropics. It is not surprising, therefore, that many have adapted to life in fresh water. On the other hand, only a few species have taken to the sea. Of the twenty-five orders into which insects are classified, twelve occur in freshwater habitats at some stage of their life-cycle. The term 'aquatic insect' covers both those that spend all their life in water, such as water bugs, as well as others, such as dragonflies, that spend only part of their life there – usually the immature stages, while the adults live on land.

The words 'insect' and 'entomology' (the study of insects) are derived respectively from the Latin *insectum* and the Greek *entomos*, both of which mean 'cut-into' and refer to the way in which insects, like other arthropods, are divided into segments. Insects differ from other arthropods in having the body separated into three well defined parts: the head, thorax and abdomen. They also have only one pair of antennae. The thorax carries the legs – never more than three pairs – and usually two pairs of wings are present on the thorax of adult insects.

Insects have two kinds of eyes: simple and compound. The simple eyes, or ocelli, are usually three in number and are located in a group on top of the head. They are probably only of use in distinguishing between light and darkness. The compound eyes are made up of many separate eyes – up to 20,000 in each compound eye in some dragonflies. What an insect sees with them is a mosaic of light and dark areas, depending on what is immediately in front of each separate lens. The main purpose is to detect movement, of prey and predator. As the eyes sometimes cover almost the whole surface of the head, the insect can receive signals from all round. If you have ever tried to approach a dragonfly, you will know that they can detect your presence some yards away, no matter from which direction you approach. Experimentally it has been shown that some species can detect a sudden movement over twelve yards away.

Insects breathe by taking in air through air-holes or 'spiracles', some on the thorax, others on the abdomen. The air is passed along flexible tubes called tracheae direct to all parts of the body needing oxygen. Although insects have blood, which carries waste products from the tissues, it is usually colourless and has little or no part to play in the process of respiration. In adult insects living in water the same process of breathing takes place, but – as we shall see later – interesting modifications of the body may be needed to suit individual species and to enable atmospheric air to be taken in at the surface and stored. Some aquatic larvae, though, have thin-walled appendages called tracheal gills to enable oxygen to be absorbed from the water. Very small larvae may be able to do this over their whole body surface.

During their development from egg to adult, insects go through several changes. In some, the larva hatched from the egg is quite unlike the adult – as, for example, the caterpillar of a butterfly. Then follows a resting and non-feeding stage called a pupa, or chrysalis. Finally the adult emerges from the pupal skin. This kind of development, with four stages, is called a 'complete metamorphosis'. In other insects the pupal stage is omitted and the larva, which resembles the adult except in size, grows continuously, with several moults, before emerging as an adult. This is known as an 'incomplete metamorphosis'. Formerly, the intermediate stage in such a life-cycle was called a nymph, but as the word has a different meaning in other languages it is now customary to use the word larva in both kinds of metamorphosis. In the later stages of the incomplete metamorphosis of aquatic insects wing-buds appear on the back of the thorax of the larva and when the final change to an adult takes place the buds expand into fully developed wings by having blood pumped into them.

The two types of metamorphosis provide a convenient means of separating groups of insects into two main divisions: Exopterygota (Greek *exo*, outside; *pterygotos*, winged), with a gradual or incomplete metamorphosis and wings developing externally; and Endopterygota (Greek *endon*, within), with a complete metamorphosis and wings developing internally.

The types of wings found in different insects have been used to divide them into orders. The scientific names of these orders (with two exceptions) end in *-ptera*, from the Greek word *pteron* meaning a wing. The following list summarises the twelve groups of insects which have representatives in or on water, beginning with a primitive group of insects which have no wings and no metamorphosis.

*APTERYGOTA:* wingless insects with no metamorphosis.
Collembola. Two species of springtails.

*PTERYGOTA:* usually with two pairs of wings and undergoing a metamorphosis.

EXOPTERYGOTA: insects with incomplete metamorphosis; wings developing externally.
Plecoptera (Greek *plekein*, to fold). Thirty-four species of stoneflies.
Ephemeroptera (Greek *ephemeros*, living for a day). Forty-seven species of mayflies.
Odonata (Greek *odontos*, a tooth, referring to the toothed jaws of the adults). Forty-four species of dragonflies.
Hemiptera (Greek *hemi*, half, referring to the fore-wings which are divided into two, the base being leathery and only the tip clear). Sixty-two species of the sub-order Heteroptera, true bugs.

ENDOPTERYGOTA: insects with a complete metamorphosis; wings developing internally.
Megaloptera (Greek *megas*, great, referring to the large wings of some species). Two species of alderflies.
Neuroptera (Greek *neuron*, a nerve. The wings have fine veins giving them the appearance of lace). One species of *Osmylus* related to the lacewings, which are also included in this order; three species of sponge flies.
Trichoptera (Greek *trichos*, a hair. The wings are covered with fine hairs). One hundred and ninety-three species of caddis flies.

Lepidoptera (Greek *lepidos*, a scale. The wings are covered with scales). Eleven species of moths.

Coleoptera (Greek *coleos*, a sheath. The fore-wings are hard and act as sheaths for the hind-wings). Three hundred species of beetles.

Diptera (Greek *di*, two). Eleven hundred species of two-winged flies (mosquitoes, midges, crane flies, etc.). Hymenoptera (Greek *hymen*, a membrane). Twenty-seven species of ichneumon flies and chalcid wasps.

Some species of aquatic insects are food for trout and other game fish, and for centuries imitations of them have been used as lures by fly-fishermen. Both the natural 'flies' and their artificial namesakes have been given traditional anglers' names and in the descriptions of the various orders of insects that follow some of these names will be included.

**Springtails** These very small primitive insects are found in damp places everywhere, but two species favour the surface film of still waters. The commoner one, *Hydropodura aquatica*, is about 1·5mm (¹/₁₆ inch) long, with a rather chubby body and a pair of short antennae. They usually congregate in great numbers on the surface and resemble particles of soot. Occasionally one will take off with a great leap and settle elsewhere – this surprising agility being due to a forked tail normally folded under the body, which can be released with some force to propel the body through the air. *Isotoma palustris* is even smaller and slimmer with longer antennae. These tiny insects are believed to feed on minute particles of plant debris.

## Insects with incomplete metamorphosis

**Stoneflies** Stoneflies are rarely found far from water. They do not fly readily even when disturbed and spend most of their short existence among stones or in the vegetation near the streams in which they pass their larval stages. They are commonest in areas where there are clear, well oxygenated, stony streams and thus more likely to be found in the northern and western areas of Britain than in the lowlands. They are easily recognised by their two long tail-filaments and long antennae.

The females lay their eggs in May and June, the larger species merely dropping the egg-mass into the water as they run over the surface, while the smaller ones dip their abdomens into the water as they fly over. The eggs drop to the bottom of the water and usually take about a month to hatch, but in some species there is a delay of up to eleven months before the larvae emerge. Most species complete their development in a year, but some of the larger species take three.

'Creeper' larva of stonefly, *Perla*

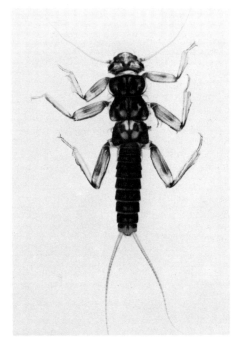

The blackish or brownish larvae are slender and, like the adults, have long tail-filaments and antennae. They live among the stones in swift streams or lakes and in silt at the bottom of slow streams, depending on the species. When full-grown, the smaller species are about 8–10mm (⅓–½ inch); the larger ones, up to 33mm (1¼ inches). The larger larvae eat both plant and animal food, but the smaller ones are vegetarian.

Careful examination of the larva of one of the bigger species will reveal tufts of thread-like gills on the thorax and near the tail-filaments, with which the insects can absorb dissolved oxygen from the water. When the concentration of oxygen is low, as it is when a larva is examined in a vessel of still water, the larva will be seen to raise and lower its body rhythmically to keep a current of water flowing over the gills. Smaller species respire through the whole body surface.

When the time for the emergence of the adult arrives, the larva crawls out of the water, usually at night, and searches for a safe place under a stone or log at the waterside. The larval skin splits at the back of the head and thorax and the perfect insect emerges. When the weather is warm and still, it may fly to the nearest tree or bush. Pairing soon takes place, then in a few days the adults die, for the larger species do not feed, although they drink water. Adults of smaller species eat lichen and algae growing on trees.

The two largest species of stonefly, *Perla bipunctata* and *Dinocras cephalotes*, are both known to fly-fishermen as the large stonefly. The females measure about 18–24mm (¾–1 inch), with heavily veined wings held close to the body and protruding beyond the end of the abdomen. The males are smaller, with shorter wings that do not reach the end of the body. Fishermen call the immature stages 'creepers'.

*Protonemura meyeri*, a stonefly that emerges early in the year, is called the early brown and is widely distributed in both lowland and upland stony streams. The yellow sally is the name given to *Isoperla grammatica*, conspicuous because of its bright yellow colour. The February red is the female of *Taeniopteryx nebulosa*, found in sluggish rivers in the north of Britain during January to March. The willow fly, *Leuctra geniculata*, on the other hand, is found in autumn on lowland rivers. A small species, *Nemoura cinerea*, only about 6mm (¼ inch) long, is abundant around ponds and its larva (about the same length) is frequently taken when pond-hunting.

**Mayflies** These insects are better known than most other aquatic insects because of their spectacular emergence in vast numbers from suitable rivers, lakes and streams in late May or early June – a phenomenon accompanied by much excitement among the fish, which rise with much splashing out of the water to snap up any within reach.

The swarms are mating flights of males; and when a female appears, some of the swarm leave the rest and follow her. Soon after copulation the females lay their eggs in the water, dipping their abdomens at the surface repeatedly – each time extruding a batch of eggs, which drop to the bottom of the water and are split into individual eggs by the force of the current. Sometimes, though, the whole mass may be dropped at once and in some species the female crawls into the water and deposits the eggs on stones. Her mission accomplished, the female dies and is washed away by the current.

Four types of mayfly larvae occur, each well adapted to the kind of habitat in which it lives. Those of the large species which carry out the spectacular emergence described above, *Ephemera vulgata* and *E. danica* – the mayfly of the fly-fisherman – are burrowers into the material at the bottom of the waters in which they live: mud in the case of *E. vulgata* or gravel and sand in the case of *E. danica*. They have flattened forelegs which can be used as shovels and dagger-like jaws which also help in the burrowing process. Active streamlined larvae like those of *Baëtis* are free-swimmers in small, stony streams. In faster streams and the wave-washed stony margins of large lakes the flattened bodies of *Ecdyonurus* enable the larvae to cling limpet-like to the undersides of stones, using their long claws to grip any irregularities in the surface. Finally, the fourth group are larvae that are sluggish in their movements and can be described as crawling larvae, since they neither burrow nor swim readily. In this group are *Ephemerella ignita*, the blue-winged olive and the small species of *Caenis*, or 'angler's curse'.

Mayfly larvae can always be distinguished from the larvae of other aquatic insects by their three tail-filaments, although in some species the middle tail disappears in the late moult and the adults that emerge have only two filaments. Other than these few species, adult mayflies all have three tail-filaments.

The larvae all have gills growing from the sides of the abdomen, tufted in some species but flat and plate-like in others. If you examine the gills of the very common species that occurs in abundance in weedy ponds, *Cloëon dipterum*, you will find that the flat gills have extensions of the tracheae or air tubes in them. It has been shown experimentally that the gills do not absorb oxygen from the water, but merely serve to act as paddles and maintain a current of water along the body to bring fresh supplies of oxygen which can be absorbed over the whole body surface. However, in badly oxygenated waters they may possibly serve to augment the supply by reverting to what must have been their original function.

All mayfly nymphs feed on algae, especially algae growing on stones, and on the debris at the bottom of the water. Adults cannot feed, as their mouth-parts are not functional.

Some species complete their metamorphosis in one year, while others even have two generations in a single year, but all species of *Ephemera* take two years. The emergence of the adults usually takes place in the evening – some at the water surface, though others come out of the water and the transformation is carried out on a stone or plant. The creature that emerges from the larval skin is not, however, fully adult but what is called a 'sub-imago', with its whole body covered in a translucent cuticle, which makes it dull in colour, and with clouded wings. In a short time this final skin is shed and the fully developed adult mayfly emerges in all its glory. Mayflies are the only insects to have a sub-imago stage.

Anglers call a sub-imago a 'dun' and the perfect imago, or adult before mating a 'spinner'. After mating, when it is floating dead or dying on the water surface, it becomes a 'spent spinner'. The names given to individual mayflies, both the natural insects and the imitations made as lures for fishing, usually indicate characteristics of colour, time of appearance and sometimes the sex of the species. Thus the male spinner of *Ephemera danica* is called the Black Drake and the female the Grey Drake, while the dun is the Green Drake. The Yellow Evening Spinner is the imago of *Ephemerella notata* and the Sherry Spinner, *E. ignita*. The March Brown, important to fly-fishermen because of its early emergence, is *Rhithrogena haarupi*.

Logically perhaps, since mayflies are not seen only in May, the insects in this group are now called 'day-flies' in angling literature. This has the partial blessing of entomologists as it follows the tradition of their Continental colleagues. They suggest, however, that the term 'mayfly' should be retained for species of *Ephemera*.

**Dragonflies** It is customary to use the word 'dragonflies' to include all the members of the order Odonata, but scientifically they are divided into two main groups or sub-orders. Zygoptera (Greek *zygon*, a yoke), the damselflies, are slender insects with weak,

Mayfly nymph, *Ephemera danica*

Flattened larva of mayfly, *Ecdyonurus*

Sub-imago stage of *Ephemera danica*

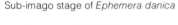

fluttering flight. Both pairs of wings are similar and are held vertically over the back when at rest. Anisoptera (Greek *anis*, unequal), the dragonflies proper, are large insects with powerful flight. Their hind wings are broader than the front and are held out horizontally when at rest. The anisopterans are sometimes divided into 'darters' (members of the family Libellulidae) and 'hawkers' (the rest), names which describe their mode of flight when catching their prey.

Both damselflies and dragonflies feed on insects which they capture in flight. Some are on the wing as early as the last week in April, but May to the end of July is the main period when they are active.

Mating takes place either while they are in flight, on the ground or resting on vegetation, depending on the species. It is one of the most remarkable ways of pairing of any insect. The male produces sperm near the tip

Common blue damselfly, *Enallagma cyathigerum*

Dragonfly, *Aeschna juncea*

of the abdomen, but has to transfer it to special pairing organs near the junction of his abdomen and thorax. This is achieved by curling his body round almost in a circle. He then seizes the female by the back of her head with a pair of claspers at the tip of his abdomen and she bends her body so that the sperm can be transferred to her abdomen from his storage organs.

The pair then fly in tandem for some time and the male often accompanies the female while she is laying her eggs. In the larger dragonflies the eggs may be merely dropped into the water as the female repeatedly dips the tip of her abdomen into the water, but some settle on floating leaves and deposit the eggs in plant tissues. Damselflies have ovipositors and lay their eggs in incisions in submerged water plants. A few fasten their eggs on the undersides of floating leaves with a sticky secretion.

The larvae of both groups of dragonflies are quite unlike the adults and spend their whole existence in water. Those of damselflies are slender-bodied and have three flat tails, which makes them easily distinguishable from other larvae in the water. As the tails have trachea or air tubes in them, they are called gills, but the larvae seem to be able to manage without them if, as sometimes happens, they are lost in an encounter with a predator. The larvae can absorb enough dissolved oxygen from the water through their whole body surface to meet their needs in normal circumstances, but possibly the gills are needed in waters deficient of oxygen.

The larvae of the larger true dragonflies are of two types. The long-bodied hawkers have larvae with long, plump bodies, while the darters have shorter-bodied larvae. Neither of these types of larva has external gills. Instead, they have them inside the rectal cavity at the rear of the body and pump fresh supplies of water inside the rectum to allow oxygen to be absorbed by the gills. When alarmed, the larvae can expel the water with considerable force, which propels them rapidly through the water – an early form of jet propulsion.

All dragonfly larvae are carnivorous and catch their prey with the 'mask', a jointed modification of the mouth parts, normally folded under the head. This can be flipped out quickly when a prey comes near and the victim grasped with the two claws at the end of the mask.

Damselfly larvae complete their metamorphosis in one year, but two years or more are usual for the hawker and darter larvae. In their later moults wing-buds appear, which increase in size with each succeeding moult. When fully grown, the larva climbs out of the water up a plant stem and soon the skin splits and the perfect insect struggles out.

The wing-buds are expanded partly by pumping blood into them, partly by the larva swallowing gulps of air. It is some time, though, before the adult insect develops its true colour and glistening wings. Some dragonflies tend to emerge at night, others in the early morning. Emergence during the day would make them more vulnerable to predation by birds, ever on the look-out for such juicy morsels.

A common and widely distributed damselfly is the common ischnura, or blue-tailed damselfly, *Ischnura elegans*, which may be seen fluttering over the vegetation of still or slow-moving waters early in the season. It has a long season, for it may appear from mid-May to the beginning of September. The dark colour of the body is relieved by lines of blue on the thorax and a blue segment near the end of the abdomen. Both sexes are similar.

Equally common and widespread is the common blue damselfly, *Enallagma cyathigerum*. The male has black segments at intervals on its blue body. The female appears much darker. Both male and female of the large red damselfly, *Pyrrhosoma nymphula*, are red all over and are often the first to be seen at the end of April. In the green lestes, or emerald damselfly, *Lestes sponsa*, both male and female are green and its favourite haunts include marshes and ditches as well as ponds and streams. It is on the wing later than the other species mentioned, appearing from the beginning of July until mid-September.

The genus *Agrion* consists of broad-winged damselflies. The banded demoiselle, *A. splendens*, has a large band of colour on the wings of the male, varying from dark brown to deep blue according to age. The female's wings are pale green. It is on the wing from mid-May to the end of September.

The best known of the hawker dragonflies is the common aeschna, *Aeschna juncea*, which flies from mid-June to mid-September. Blue spots all along the body of the male relieve the dark brown general colouring, though they may turn to green or yellow with age. The female is more drably coloured, with a lighter brown overall colour with green or yellow spots.

The common aeschna is a powerful flyer, hawking along its favourite 'beat' until late in the evening in search of gnats and other flies that are abundant then.

Perhaps the most widely distributed of the darter dragonflies is the four-spotted libellula, *Libellula quadrimaculata*, which appears in mid-May and flies until the end of August or later. The swift, darting flight distinguishes it from the continuous flying of the hawkers. Seen at close quarters, it will be noticed that the body is shorter and the abdomen flatter. The general body colouring is brown, with yellow along the outer edges, and both sexes are alike. The dark spots on each of the four wings, from which the second of its scientific names derives, identify it clearly.

Of the forty-four species of dragonflies in Britain, seventeen are included in the sub-order Zygoptera and twenty-seven in Anisoptera.

These insects were regarded with some suspicion in earlier days, as their traditional names 'horse-stingers' and 'Devil's darning needles' imply. However, they are perfectly harmless and cannot sting either horses or any other animal. On the contrary, they perform a useful service for us by feeding on insects that do bite, especially mosquitoes and similar insects.

**Water bugs**  To the uninitiated all insects are 'bugs', but to entomologists a bug is a member of the order Hemiptera. These insects have beak-like mouth parts adapted for piercing and for sucking up liquids – either plant juices or the body fluids of animals, depending on the kind of bug. This beak-like structure, called the rostrum, has inside it needle-like stylets which are plunged into plant or animal tissue. Land bugs include many pests familiar to plant growers, including aphids and cuckoo-spit insects, but these belong to the sub-order Homoptera and are outside our concern here. Included in the sub-order Heteroptera are bugs that live on or in water. These still retain certain of the characteristics of land insects, particularly the need to breathe atmospheric air, and some do not live in the water at any stage but on the surface film, where they find a plentiful supply of food in the form of small creatures that have fallen there accidentally and a welcome freedom from predators that would attack them if they lived on land. All water bugs pass through an incomplete metamorphosis of egg, larva and adult and are carnivorous.

Usually the first insects you see when approaching a pond are the various species of pond skaters or water striders as they are sometimes called, of the genus *Gerris* (or *Aquarius*, as some are now named). If the insects are on clear water and the day is sunny, you will notice the shadows cast on the bottom by the dimples they make in the surface film. About 15mm (⅔ inch) in

Water measurer, *Hydrometra*

length, they skate quickly and confidently over the surface film, as if it was ice, using their long middle legs to propel them. The front legs are shorter and used mainly for capturing prey, while the hind legs probably maintain stability and help to steer. The legs are modified in an interesting way. The claws, which in most insects are at the very tip of the legs, are in pond skaters a short distance up the leg, where they cannot penetrate the surface film. The tips of the legs also have a pad of water-repellent hairs so they do not break the film. Sometimes a bubble of air is trapped in the hairs and may act as a float. Pond skaters are sensitive to movements on the water, so they soon notice the struggles of a drowning insect which has fallen onto the surface and the insect is quickly caught and eaten.

Pond skaters spend the winter away from the water and reappear in late April or early May, when they start to mate, though mating continues for much of the summer. Eggs are laid in gelatinous masses on vegetation below the water surface. There are winged and wingless individuals, as well as some with very small wings, in this family of bugs. The winged forms appear amazingly quickly on a newly constructed garden pond.

A much smaller and thinner insect can be found on the surface of the water at the edge of a pond. It moves so slowly that it has earned the name water measurer, *Hydrometra*, for it seems to pace out the distance as it walks over the surface film. The incredibly thin body is about 12mm (½ inch) in length, with an elongated head, eyes set well back from the front of the body and long legs and antennae. The front legs are unable to grasp prey, as can those of a pond skater, but the insect manages to feed on dead insects on the surface and also impales small animals below the surface, such as water fleas and gnat larvae, and sucks out their body fluids. Winged individuals are very rare.

Water scorpion

Saucer bug, *Ilyocoris cimicoides*

Egg-laying starts in mid-May and probably continues for some weeks. The eggs are laid singly on plant stems above water and are attached at right angles to the support.

The lively little water crickets, *Velia*, usually found in groups on ponds, ditches and slow streams, are only about 7mm (⅓ inch) long and have shorter legs than the other bugs mentioned in this chapter. The general colouring of the body is brown, but two red stripes run the length of the abdomen and the underside is orange. There are both winged and wingless individuals. Their eggs are laid in rows on waterside plants.

The water scorpions are beautifully adapted for life in water. The commoner species, *Nepa cinerea*, is about 25mm (1 inch) long. It is very flat and can easily be mistaken for a dead leaf on the bottom of a pond, especially as it feigns death when disturbed. The most striking feature of the water scorpion is the long tube at the rear end of the body which, since it looks like a sting, has earned the insect its name. The tube is about 8mm (⅓ inch) long and is made up of two separate halves held together by hooked bristles along their sides. The tube is not a sting, however, but a 'snorkel' which can be pushed to the surface of the water to take in air for the spiracles at the end of the body, and to the other spir-

acles by grooves along the abdomen. The breathing-tube has water-repellent hairs at the tip to prevent it being waterlogged.

The two front legs are modified into grasping organs, by means of which prey is caught and held while its body fluids are sucked out through the rostrum. Any small animals that come within reach of the claws are grabbed. The leathery front wings act as sheaths for the pair of membranous wings folded underneath them, but the wing muscles are not fully developed in most individuals and very few water scorpions of this species can fly.

Eggs are laid singly in spring in incisions made by the female in the stems of submerged

*Aphelocheirus montandoni*

Water boatman, *Notonecta* sp.

*Corixa punctata*

Alderfly

water plants. Up to thirty-two have been counted, laid in one night by a single female. Each egg has between seven and nine thread-like tubes at its free end, which are believed to absorb oxygen from the water for the developing embryo.

The less common long water scorpion, *Ranatra linearis*, is found among water plants at the edge of ponds in the southern counties of Britain. Since it also can feign death, it can be mistaken for a dead stick, too. The body is about 35mm (1⅝ inch) long and the breathing tube another 25mm (1 inch) long, but instead of being flat, as in the commoner species, the body is cylindrical.

The eggs are laid in rows in incisions in submerged plants but have only two thread-like tubes at their free ends. The larvae of both water scorpions have very small breathing-tubes at first and hang down from the surface by their legs, with the tip of the tube just above the water level.

Surprisingly for such an ungainly animal, the long water scorpion flies quite readily when conditions become unsuitable and it has to seek out a new stretch of water.

The saucer bug, *Ilyocoris cimicoides*, which has an oval body about 15mm (⅗ inch) long, is fairly common in weedy ponds in southern counties. It is fiercely carnivorous and can give a painful prick with its rostrum to anyone handling it. Eggs are deposited in rows in the submerged stems of water plants from late April to the end of May. Although it has well developed wings, it has never been observed to fly. But it can walk rapidly and, presumably, that is how it finds its way to new ponds.

In this insect we have a form of air store that, with variations, will be found in many of the insects described in this chapter. Bubbles of air are held by hairs in a cavity between the wing-cases and the upper surface of the abdomen, and also on the underside of the abdomen. Spiracles adjoining the bubbles enable the air to reach all parts of the body through the tracheal tubes. The air supply is renewed at intervals by a visit to the water surface, but these air bubbles can act as a kind of gill. As oxygen is used up by the insect, more can diffuse in from the water to maintain the pressure within. Eventually the bubble gets smaller through the continuous diffusion outwards of nitrogen and the insect has to rise to the surface to renew the bubble.

A water bug with an even more efficient type of air supply, which enables it to live in water without ever having to come to the surface, is *Aphelocheirus montandoni*. Because it is not a very well known insect it has not received a popular name. It is about 11mm (½ inch) long and lives in moderately fast, stony streams, mostly in the south of Britain. Both the upper and lower sides of the body are covered with a pile of very fine, unwettable hairs, bent over at their tips and set so close together that it has been estimated that there are over two million hairs to the square millimetre. With such a dense pile the film of air, only one molecule thick, is not lost when the pressure inside decreases through the respiration of the insect, and oxygen continually diffuses into the film from the surrounding water. The gas store is in contact with specially adapted rosette-shaped spiracles. Such a form of air store is called a plastron (from the French *plastron*, a breast-plate).

A further modification in this remarkable

insect is that the pair of spiracles on the second abdominal segment open into collapsible air sacs. Connected to them are sense organs that are sensitive to changes of pressure. It is believed that these warn the insect of places in the water where there is a low pressure of oxygen which would reduce the effectiveness of the plastron. For this reason, streams with well oxygenated water are necessary for the survival of *Aphelocheirus*.

The female lays her eggs in late spring and attaches them to stones. The larvae do not have a plastron, respiration taking place directly through the skin.

*Aphelocheirus* cannot fly, but swims well. It spends most of its time walking about on the bottom of the stream in search of the aquatic larvae on which it feeds.

The water boatmen, or back-swimmers, are familiar insects in ponds, ditches and canals. They are often seen floating at the surface, upside down, with the tip of the abdomen tilted to touch the surface film, taking in air. Their air supply is held by long rows of bristles on the abdomen, forming two passages, one on each side. The bubble makes them very buoyant, so when they need to rest they have to hold on to plants or other objects under the water. Water boatmen swim actively, helped by the long bristles that fringe their hind legs, making them into efficient oars. The likeness to a boat is completed by the smooth, streamlined body.

The most widely distributed water boatman is *Notonecta glauca*, adults of which are about 15mm (³/₅ inch) long. Eggs are laid early in the year, even in February, the long, oval eggs being placed horizontally in submerged stems of water plants. In *N. maculata*, a species common in the southern counties, the eggs are attached to a stone or other solid support. The larvae of water boatmen are pale in colour and some have red eyes. Not so buoyant as the adults, they spend much of their time at the bottom of the water.

Water boatmen are fierce predators of anything they can catch and even attack small fish much larger than themselves. Care should be taken in handling them, for their rostrum and the toxic saliva that it injects can cause a painful wound. As they fly readily in warm weather, they soon find new garden ponds, where they can be troublesome, attacking fish.

There are many species of the lesser water boatmen belonging to the family Corixidae. They are smaller than the water boatmen and can always be distinguished from them since they do not swim upside down. Usually they are found near the bottom of the water, for they feed in a different manner from water boatmen, using their rostrum rather like a vacuum cleaner, sucking up algae and plant debris.

Corixids occur in all kinds of freshwater habitats, even in brackish waters, but each species has its special preference for particular conditions, especially the degree of silting. As a pond or other habitat becomes more silted, there is a definite succession of different species living in it.

The round eggs are attached to the surface of submerged plants as early as January. The larvae do not have an air store until they reach their third moult, but they can obtain sufficient oxygen for their needs.

The commonest species, *Corixa punctata*, about 13mm (½ inch) long, is usually found in weedy ponds. It is a ready flier and frequently searches for new habitats. Small pea-shell cockles have been found attached to the legs of this corixid, a good example of the way in which freshwater animals are dispersed to new sites.

## Insects with a complete metamorphosis

**Alderflies**  Alderflies are familiar insects in May and June around ponds, streams and lakes. There are two species, though little is known about one of them. The common species, *Sialis lutaria*, is dark brown in colour and has dull, heavily veined wings, which are held ridged over the back, like the roof of a house, when the insect is not flying, and long antennae. The females, which are a little larger than the males, are about 13mm (½ inch) long. The insects are usually to be seen resting on waterside vegetation or stones. If disturbed, they reluctantly take to the wing.

The female lays her eggs in clusters either as a flat mass or encircling a plant stem. Up to nine hundred eggs may be laid by a single female. Each egg is cigar-shaped with a 'pedicel', or stalk-like structure, at the free end. As soon as the larva emerges from the

Larva of alderfly

Sponge fly larva, *Sisyra*

egg, it makes for the water – often simply dropping into it, as the eggs are usually on plants overhanging the water.

The larvae are easily distinguishable, having seven pairs of tube-like tracheal gills on the sides of the abdomen. These are carried upright, pointing slightly backwards. The end of the body tapers to a point. When full-grown, the larva is about 25mm (1 inch) long. Frequently the larva undulates its body rhythmically to create a current of fresh water over its gills. It spends most of its time in the mud or silt at the bottom of the water searching for the worms and midge larvae ('bloodworms') on which it mainly feeds, although it eats mayfly larvae and caddis larvae, too.

The larval stage lasts nearly two years, involving about ten moults. Eventually, at any time from March to June, the larva crawls out of the water and excavates a chamber about half an inch below the surface of the soil, possibly some distance from the pond or stream, and pupates. The length of the pupal stage varies with the temperature, but is usually about three weeks. The imago emerges in the early morning and the new generation of alderflies is on the wing from late April until July.

Much rarer is *S. fuliginosa*. The adults are blacker than the common species and are on the wing rather later. The larvae favour faster streams or the upper reaches of rivers.

To the angler the alderfly is known as the orl fly and an imitation of the adult fly is used when the alders are on the wing. Trout eat many of the true insects when they drop onto the surface exhausted or after mating and laying eggs.

**Sponge flies**  These small insects are relatives of the green lacewing flies sometimes seen in our gardens or houses in summer, but they are much smaller. The larvae are parasites of freshwater sponges, using tube-like mouth parts to suck out their body fluids. Three species have been found in Britain.

The body of the larva is plump, but tapers towards the tail end, and from each segment of the body grow tufts of bristles. Seven pairs of finger-like tracheal gills are on the underside of the abdomen.

The common species is *Sisyra fuscata*. The adult flies are about 6mm (¼ inch) long, brown in colour, and are on the wing in May and June and found around ponds, canals and slow rivers where sponges are living. The eggs are laid in small clusters on plants or artificial structures, such as the walls of canal locks, where they will overhang the water. The larvae hatch in about a fortnight and fall into the water, drifting about for a time until they encounter a sponge on which they immediately begin to feed. When full-grown, they leave the water and pupate in a suitable crevice in the bark of a tree by the waterside or in the wall of a lock or bridge. They spin a silken cocoon about 4mm (⅙ inch) in which to spend the pupal stage.

Larvae which have grown quickly through the summer complete their life-cycle in the year they are hatched and emerge as adult flies in August or September. Others which have not developed so quickly during the summer spend the winter in their cocoons as a stage called a 'prepupa' and only pupate fully the following spring, changing to adults in May or June the year after they were hatched.

**Caddis flies**  The larvae or 'grubs' of caddis flies are well known to anyone who has taken part in pond-hunting expeditions, because of the cases made of sticks, stones or other materials which they live in and carry about with them. Few people, however, know the adult caddis flies, since most of them come out only at dusk or during the night and even then can easily be mistaken for small moths. Close examination of an adult caddis fly reveals one great difference for their wings are covered with small hairs, instead of scales as in moths, a feature referred to in the name of this order of insects, Trichoptera ('hairy-winged').

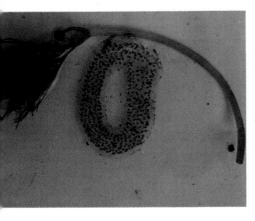

Egg-mass of caddis fly, *Phryganea grandis*

Caddis fly, *Glyphotaelius pellucidus*

The wings of caddis are long and narrow, with the fore wings slightly longer than the hind wings, and their colouring drab, with patterns of brown predominating. The antennae, which are long and many-jointed, are held out in front of the head. Since their mouth parts are poorly developed, caddis can feed only on nectar and plant juices, so their adult life is brief and is spent mainly near the pond, stream or lake where they passed their larval stages. The life-cycle is similar in all species – except that some small ones may have two generations in a year, whereas most have only one.

Of nearly two hundred species of caddis in Britain forty-seven do not make cases at the larval stage. These will be described later.

The eggs of caddis flies are usually laid in a mass and covered with a jelly-like material. Some females deposit the eggs on a leaf above the water surface, but others enter the water and fasten the eggs to a stone. Members of the family Phryganeidae bend the egg-mass into a circle and attach it vertically to floating leaves of water plants.

As soon as the tiny larva hatches from the egg, if it is one of the species that make cases, it produces from a gland near the mouth a sticky secretion which it winds round itself, attaching small pieces of plant debris or sand grains until its body is covered. As it grows, new material is added at the head end. When alarmed, the larva withdraws quickly into the case, with its head blocking the entrance. But when searching for food, the head, thorax and legs are extended out of the case, leaving the soft and vulnerable abdomen within. A pair of hooks at the rear end of the body hold the larva firmly in its case.

Most case-building larvae feed on plant material, although a few occasionally eat animal food. Their excursions along the bottom mud or among the water plants has therefore a dual purpose: finding food and selecting materials to extend the case. Each species make a characteristic case and it is usually possible to identify them from their cases alone. Care must be taken in identification, however, because when the right materials are not available – as, for instance, in an aquarium – the larva will make its case from whatever is available.

Larvae have tracheal gills along the body, but it is believed that they can absorb oxygen from the water through their body surface, at least when they are small, and they are often to be seen undulating their body in the case to keep a current of fresh water circulating through it.

Perhaps the commonest kinds of larval case found in ponds and ditches are those made of carefully measured lengths of plant stem, especially rushes, arranged across the case. These are made by some of the many species of *Limnephilus*, such as *L. rhombicus* and *L. marmoratus*. A beautiful, neater and often more colourful case is that of members of the family Phryganeidae. It is made of vegetable material cut into uniform lengths, wrapped spirally round the case. *Anabolia nervosa* makes a cylindrical case of sand grains and cements to it one or more long twigs far exceeding the length of the main case. It has been suggested that this unusual form is intended to deter fish, especially trout, from making a meal of the larvae, as it would be almost impossible to swallow such a difficult mouthful. The species occurs in streams, as well as ponds.

Some larvae living in fast streams make cases, usually from sand grains. That of *Molanna angustata* cannot be mistaken, for attached to the sides of the conical sand-grain case are flat extensions of the same material, while a smooth, curved case is made by *Odontocerum albicorne*. On the undersides of stones in small streams the tortoiseshell-shaped cases of *Agapetus fuscipes* will usually be found in spring. Here, too, will be found stony cases with larger stones attached made by *Silo pallipes*. In slower streams a similar case made by an allied species, *Goera pilosa*, occurs. But perhaps the commonest of all cases made by stream caddis is the largish tubular case of larger grains made by *Potamophylax stellatus*.

As mentioned previously, not all caddis larvae make cases. The larva of *Rhyacophila* creeps about under stones in streams, hunting for the larvae of other insects on which it feeds. This larva is greenish or yellowish and has prominent tufts of tracheal tubes on the sides of the body.

Most species that do not make cases spin nets in streams and rivers into which food, in the form of particles of debris or small animals, is swept and becomes trapped. The species of the genus *Hydropsyche* live in rapid streams and their nets can often be seen on the moss-covered surfaces of stones. The nets are usually set across or at an angle to the water current. The larvae of Philoptamidae make long tubular nets with small openings which are spun across spaces between large stones. Galleries of tunnels constructed from particles of all kinds, cemented together with silk, are made by species of the genus *Tinodes*.

The larval period lasts about a year and when the time for pupation comes even species that do not normally live in cases make them for the pupal stage, sometimes fastening them to larger stones if they are in fast streams to prevent them being washed away by the current. The pupa may remain in its case over the winter in some species.

The pupae have strong jaws with which to bite their way out of the case, for before pupating the larva will have covered the entrance with some form of grating, which while protecting it from intruders allows a current of water to circulate through the case. Having bitten its way out of the case, the pupa swims to the surface; for, unusually among insect pupae, those of caddis flies have strong legs for this purpose. The emergence of the adult insect may take place as soon as the pupa reaches the surface and it flies off from the cast pupal skin floating on the water. Other pupae crawl out of the water and the change takes place at the waterside. Some species of caddis produce scents (called phero-mones) that are thought to be of use in finding mates.

Unfortunately, few caddis flies have been given English names, except by anglers, and these are often applied to more than one species. The Large Red Sedge can be any species of *Phryganea*; the Brown Sedge is *Anabolia nervosa*; the Grannom, *Brachycentrus subnubilus*; the Welshman's Button,

*Sericosioma personatum*; the Black Silverhorns, *Athripsodes aterrimus*; and the Brown Silverhorns, *A. cinereus*. The name Cinnamon Sedge is used for many medium-sized caddis which have brown wings and green or brown abdomens. The Caperer is the name given to *Halesus radiatus*, which is an autumn species. To the angler all caddis flies are 'sedge flies'.

Caddis at all stages are important food for trout. The larvae, the pupae swimming to the surface, the freshly emerged imago, while it is still resting on the water, the females laying their eggs and both males and females when they are lying dead or dying on the surface are all avidly taken. If attempts to suck them out of their cases fail the trout swallow them as well, except those of *Anabolia nervosa*, already mentioned, which can crawl freely over the riverbed with impunity.

Larva stream caddis, *Rhyacophila*

China-mark moths: **left,** *Nymphula nymphaeta*; **right,** *Catalclysta lemnata*

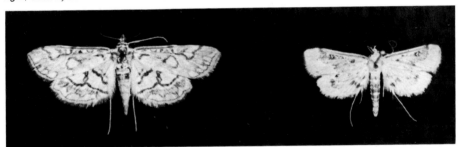

**Aquatic moths** A pond is, perhaps, a strange place in which to find caterpillars of moths – but a few species of the family Pyralidae have adapted in varying degrees to life under water in their early stages and one species in particular is very common and widely distributed, though often overlooked. The adult moths are called china-mark moths, because the markings on the wings of some of them are supposed to look like the potters' marks on porcelain.

The presence of the caterpillars of the brown china-mark moth, *Nymphula nymphaeata*, can often be detected in summer by oval holes, about 25mm (1 inch) long, cut in the floating leaves of water-lilies and floating pondweed. If these damaged leaves are turned over, the missing pieces may be found with small caterpillars between them and the leaf, the case so formed being attached by silk.

From June to August the adult moths are on the wing at dusk, but in the daytime they are hidden in the waterside vegetation. The wings, which are about 30mm (1¼ inches) across, are richly patterned in brown and white. The female lays her eggs about June, usually depositing them in a flat mass on the underside of floating leaves. They hatch in about a fortnight. At first the caterpillar burrows into the undersides of leaves, then after a few days it cuts a small oval piece of leaf and fastens it with silk at the edges to the leaf. At this stage the caterpillar is quite wet and presumably obtains its oxygen all over its body from the water. After several moults the body becomes covered with fine hairs and, if you open a larval case at this stage, you will find the caterpillar is now quite dry and the case sealed at its edges with silk. It is now breathing air trapped in its case and even when the caterpillar puts its head out to feed on the leaf no water can get into the case because the aperture is so small, and the hairs prevent water from entering. The caterpillar pupates in a silken cocoon within the case, fastened by silk to a plant stem just above the water surface.

A smaller species, *Cataclysta lemnata*, has a similar life history but lives among duckweed. The ringed china-mark, *Parapoynx stratiotata*, a larger species but not so common, feeds on a variety of submerged plants, spinning an open web in the leaves and stems in which to live. Its spiracles are closed and it has external tracheal gills so that it can take in oxygen from the water. Pupation also takes place under water.

**Beetles** The order Coleoptera ('sheathed-winged') is divided into two sub-orders: Adephaga (Greek *aden*, abundantly; *phagos*, eating) are mainly voracious carnivores; and Polyphaga (Greek *poly*, many) mainly omnivores. The feeding habits of both larvae and adults vary in different species.

Good examples of the Adephaga are the various species of *Dytiscus*, the diving beetles, of which *D. marginalis*, the great diving beetle, is the best known. None has been more successful in adapting to a life in water than this beetle and its close relatives. Its streamlined body, smooth wing-cases (in the

Leaf of floating pondweed with the larval case of a china mark moth and the oval hole in the edge of the leaf from which the case was made.

Caterpillar of *Paraponyx stratiotata*

Female great diving beetle breathing at the surface

Great diving beetle, *Dytiscus marginalis*

Sucker-pad of male diving beetle

male, at any rate) and its strong hind legs, fringed with bristles to effect rapid movement through the water in search of prey, make it a formidable member of the freshwater fauna, ready to attack creatures much larger than itself, even fish. About 35mm (1²⁄₅ inch) long, it is olive-brown in colour and is named *marginalis* because of the yellow margin to the wing-cases and thorax. The wing-cases of the female are furrowed along their length and another distinction between the sexes is that the first three segments of the tarsus (foot) of the front legs in the male are expanded into a pad with two large suckers and many small ones. These can secrete a sticky substance and are used to hold on to the thorax of the female while pairing.

These beetles fly readily and soon find their way into garden ponds, where they can do a lot of damage to fish and other creatures. The flights take place mainly at night and many beetles come to grief by mistaking a wet road or the roof of a greenhouse for a pond.

The position of air stores in insects determines which part of the body is the most buoyant. In *Dytiscus* the air is stored under the wing-cases and on the abdomen, so that when it stops swimming it automatically floats to the surface, with the end of the abdomen just above the water level. This brings two spiracles, larger than those on the rest of the body, into contact with the air and provides an immediate supply. It can also renew the bubble of air held by the hairs on the abdomen by lifting the wing-cases slightly.

In early spring the female lays her cigar-shaped eggs in slits made in submerged plants. From these hatch larvae with a long body and a pair of powerful sickle-shaped jaws, which are hollow. When prey is caught, a digestive liquid is pumped into the body of the victim to dissolve its body-contents, then sucked back, leaving only an empty skin. The larva has to make frequent visits to the surface for air, as it has no air store. Two tail appendages fringed with hair enable it to remain attached

Larva of great diving beetle

Larva of whirligig beetle

to the surface film while it takes in air at the two spiracles at the end of the abdomen. The other seven pairs of spiracles along the body of the larva are closed and do not become functional until the pupal stage.

When full-grown, the larva is about 50mm (2 inches) long. It then crawls out of the water and makes an oval cell in the moist earth near the edge of the water in which to pupate. The pupal stage usually takes about a fortnight to three weeks, but the newly emerged adult may wait a little longer in the cell to let its integument harden. As full-grown larvae are sometimes found in May and June, it seems possible that some are not ready for pupation at the end of summer and over-winter as larvae.

There are many other smaller members of the family Dytiscidae. Perhaps the best known of these is *Acilius sulcatus*. The adults are about 16mm (³/₅ inch) in length and are easily identified by the broad black bands on the head and thorax, the general colouring being brown. The larva, although similar to that of *Dytiscus*, has the first segment of the thorax greatly lengthened so that it looks like a long neck.

Also included in Adephaga are the whirligig beetles, species of the genus *Gyrinus*. These small oval beetles, the commonest being about 7mm (¼ inch), have very shiny, black wing-cases. They are usually seen swimming, many together, on the surface of ponds, ditches and slow streams, whirling around rapidly in all directions. Their great speed is achieved by means of an interesting modification of the middle and hind legs, which are very flat and fringed with hair. When expanded, the flat surfaces make highly efficient paddles; but they can fold up when the legs are drawn back in preparation for the next swimming stroke, thus presenting little resistance to the water. The action is analogous to 'feathering' oars in rowing. Their eyes, too, are modified for life on the surface film, each compound eye being divided into two parts, one able to see objects above the surface and the other what is below. Whirligigs feed on insects that have fallen on to the water, but also dive after prey below the surface. In such cases, and when they are alarmed, they carry down with them a small bubble of air at the end of the abdomen. They also have an air store under the wing-cases.

The female lays small cylindrical eggs in batches on the leaves of submerged plants. The larva is long and flattened with long tracheal gills along the sides of the body. When it is full-grown it is about 15mm (³/₅ inch) long. It then climbs out of the water up a plant stem and makes an oval cocoon in which to pupate.

In ponds rich in decaying matter may be found a small beetle about 12mm (½ inch) long that draws attention to itself when caught in a net by making a squeaking sound. This is the screech beetle, *Hygrobia hermanni*, and it makes the noise by rubbing the rough surface of the undersides of the wing-cases against the edge of the abdomen. The larva is very distinctive, with a large head end to the body, which tapers towards the three tail-filaments. It spends its time mainly in the mud, searching for the bloodworms on which it feeds. Pupation takes place in the soil at the edge of the pond.

The sub-order Polyphaga includes the largest water beetle, the great silver beetle, *Hydrophilus piceus*, now a very rare insect since many of the drainage dykes in the south of England where it was found have been cleared of vegetation in order to provide irrigation for farm land. The beetles are about 45mm (1¾ inches) long and are greenish-black in colour. In the male the end joint of the front legs is flattened into a triangular plate. The common name refers to the large bubble of air covering the underside of the thorax and front part of the abdomen in both sexes, which under water gives a silvery appearance. There is also an air store under the wing-cases. The silvery bubble on the underside is in two parts – one held by a pile of minute, closely packed hairs and the other by longer, flexible hairs bent over parallel to the body surface. In winter, when the beetle is inactive, the bubble held by the small hairs probably provides an adequate supply of oxygen. But in summer, when more oxygen is needed, the insect rises to the surface to renew its air stores, both on the longer hairs on its underside and under its wing-cases. The beetle spends much time

**Above** *Acilius sulcatus*

**Right** Great silver beetle, *Hydrophilus piceus*

**Below** Whirligig beetle, *Gyrinus* sp.

Great silver beetle, *Hydrophilus*, renewing its air supply at the surface

Egg-case of great silver beetle

grooming the large air bubbles with its legs.

Unlike the diving beetles, the silver beetle rises to the surface head first and breaks the surface film with its club-shaped antennae. Fringes of hair on the head and antennae then form a channel to bring the bubbles into communication with the atmosphere.

Silver beetles swim in a slow and laboured manner, using the swimming legs alternately, unlike diving beetles, whose legs work in unison. The silver beetles, however, have no need of rapid movement, for they spend much of their time browsing on submerged water plants, although they do eat animal food when they get the chance.

The female lays about 50 eggs in an oval case, which she spins of silk. This has a hollow section at one end, probably designed to maintain an air supply for the developing eggs and, later, for the larvae when they first hatch. Although the egg-case can float freely, surface tension seems to cause it to be strongly attracted to plants or other supports above the surface. In about a fortnight the larvae bite their way out of the case and fall into the water. They are entirely carnivorous, feeding mainly on water snails. By the end of the summer they are about 64mm (2½ inches) long and very fat. They leave the water to pupate in a cell excavated in damp soil near the water's edge. The adult beetle emerges in about six weeks and returns to the water.

A smaller relative of the silver beetle, with similar habits, is *Hydrochara caraboides*. This is greenish-black in colour and about 15 mm (³⁄₅ inch) long. *Helochares lividus*, a yellow beetle about 6mm (¼ inch) long, found in ponds and ditches, has the unusual habit of carrying its eggs in a little bag attached to the abdomen.

A few species of the large family Chrysomelidae, the leaf beetles, can be seen around ponds and streams in summer, where they attract attention with their brilliant metallic colours. *Donacia crassipes*, which is green and about 12mm (½ inch) long, is found on water-lilies; *D. aquatica* has red wing-cases with green edges and is found on a number of different plants.

The females lay their eggs on the undersides of leaves at the waterside, first cutting a hole in the leaf, then placing the abdomen through it to deposit the eggs. When the larvae hatch, they drop to the bottom of the water, where they attach themselves to the rhizomes and roots of the plants and tap the supply of food there. They are grub-like creatures and do not move about much. At the end of the abdomen they have hollow spines with which they penetrate the plant to tap the supply of air in the air spaces for their own use. They pupate in a silken cocoon attached to the root or rhizome, from which they continue to obtain their air supply through small holes they have made. This must provide more than enough air for their immediate needs; for when the adult beetle emerges in the spring, it reaches the surface of the water quite unwetted in an envelope of air and is able to fly immediately.

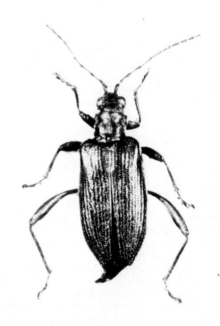

Leaf beetle, *Donacia crassipes*

Pupal cases of *Donacia* on the rhizome of reed, *Phragmites*

Larvae and pupae of the mosquito, *Culex*

**Two-winged flies** Diptera is a huge order of insects, including such familiar ones as house flies, bluebottles, mosquitoes and hover flies. Most insects have four wings, but the hind wings of flies are reduced to small club-shaped stalks called halteres or 'balancers', because if deprived of them the insects cannot control their flight. The halteres can be seen quite easily on a large insect such as a daddy-long-legs or crane fly.

Crane flies belong to the first of the sub-orders into which Diptera is divided, the Nematocera (Greek *nematos*, a thread; *keras*, a horn) or 'thread-horns', insects with long, slender many-jointed antennae. 'Leather-jackets', which do so much damage by eating the roots of crops, are crane-fly larvae. Others live in damp ground at the margins of streams or even in the water, feeding on decaying vegetation. They are grub-like creatures, dirty-white or brown in colour. When full-grown, they may measure up to 30mm (1¼ inches) in length. They have tube-like gills at the rear end of the body and in the genus *Tipula* an irregularly shaped plate there bearing spiracles. The pupae, which are shorter, have a pair of horns on the head for respiration.

*Ptychoptera*, a member of a related family, has a very curious larva ending in a long, tail-like breathing tube with two tracheae running through it. It can be shortened or lengthened to suit the depth of water where it is living. Usually the larva lives in the mud, from which it eats particles of decaying plant material. This larva should not be mistaken for the rat-tailed maggot of drone flies mentioned later in the chapter.

The larvae and pupae of gnats and mosquitoes are some of the most abundant insects not only in ponds but in small bodies of water such as water butts and horse troughs, and are

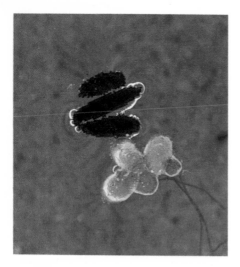

Egg-raft of common gnat, *Culex pipiens*. The plant is lesser duckweed.

among the first arrivals in a newly made garden pond. Twenty-six species of culicine mosquitoes and four species of anopheline mosquitoes occur in Britain. They all have similar life histories. Eggs are laid by the females on the surface of the water, in the culicines in unsinkable rafts of about two hundred and singly by the anophelines. The larvae of culicines rest almost vertically at the surface with the breathing-tube at the rear end of the body held in the surface film by five small flaps at its tip which open out into a kind of funnel. In *Anopheles* the larva rests horizontally at the surface taking in air through spiracles on the eighth abdominal segment.

While they are resting, vibrating mouth-brushes, in both kinds of larvae, create currents in the water which bring minute organisms to the mouth. In about three weeks the larvae change to pupae, shaped like a comma, with a large head on which are two short tubes. The pupae do not feed, but remain at the surface taking in air down the tubes. Eventually the skin splits at the top of the head and the perfect fly emerges, then rests for a while on the discarded pupal skin before flying away to mate.

Only the female insects have piercing mouth parts for sucking blood, which they need before they can lay eggs. The males feed on nectar and other plant juices.

*Culex pipiens*, the commonest species, does not attack humans but is troublesome to birds. *Theobaldia annulata*, which has speckled legs and dark spots on the wings, is the one that produces the worst gnat-bites. The species of *Aedes*, whose larvae resemble those of *Culex*, are very common and attack humans. *Anopheles maculipennis*, which breeds in brackish water such as pools in coastal areas, can transmit the malaria parasite. Indeed, malaria – or ague, as it was called – was common in coastal areas of Britain at one time and could become a danger again, now that holidaymakers are contracting the disease abroad and providing a reservoir of parasites in Britain. Garden pools are happily safe from *Anopheles maculipennis* and providing fish, especially golden orfe, which are surface feeders, are kept in them, few biting insects will survive to the adult stage.

Closely related to the mosquito are the four species of *Chaoborus*, sometimes called phantom midges, although they are not true midges. The larva is a transparent creature about 12mm (½ inch) long when full-grown. It floats horizontally in the water. With a jerk of the body it can vanish and reappear some distance away. This behaviour and its extreme transparency have earned the larvae the name of 'ghost' or 'phantom' larvae. Two pairs of dark sausage-shaped air sacs, one at each end of the body, are hydrostatic organs, which enable the larva to control its buoyancy. When the larva rises in the water the bladders are distended and when it sinks they contract. Respiration is carried out through the whole body surface.

The prey consists of small crustaceans and other tiny animals, caught by the specially

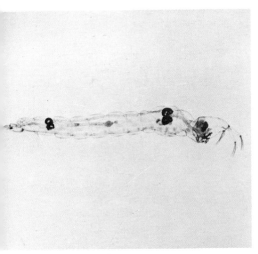

Phantom larva, *Chaoborus*

Egg-mass of *Chaoborus*

modified antennae which have become grasping organs. Phantom larvae can be found in ponds throughout the winter. The pupae are like those of the mosquitoes. The females lay their eggs in flat spiral masses in a gelatinous covering.

The non-biting midges make up a large family, Chironomidae, with about four hundred species. Their worm-like larvae exist in immense numbers in all freshwater habitats and are one of the most important sources of food for larger animals. The mating swarm of males is a common feature in all the Nematocera, but in the Chironomidae it is often spectacular. Immense swarms can be seen on summer evenings over waters where they have been living and they often congregate over some prominent object in the landscape such as a tall tree or church steeple. From a distance the swarms look like smoke and have often caused alarm. After a female has joined the swarm and pairing has taken place, she lays a rope of eggs enclosed in jelly on a plant or other support near the water.

Chironomid larvae vary greatly in colour. Some may be almost transparent, others brownish or greenish. Such species are usually

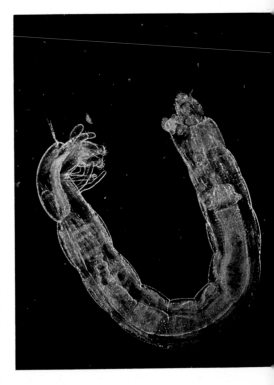

Larva of a chironomid fly

found living freely in the water or among vegetation and swim by making violent contortions of the body. The largest species are in the genus *Chironomus* and may be up to 20mm (⁴/₅ inch) long. They are usually red in colour and live in tubes of detritus bound together with silk and attached to the bottom mud or other support. The larvae frequently leave the tubes for short periods and soon make new ones if disturbed. These red larvae are called 'bloodworms' and they have in their blood the red respiratory pigment haemoglobin. In well oxygenated waters this seems to take no part in respiration and the larvae, in common with those of other colours, absorb the oxygen they require from the water through their skins. However, many bloodworms live in waters that are low in oxygen and the haemoglobin is then of value in making the most of what little oxygen is available and enables them to survive in these adverse conditions. The tubular structures at the rear of the body which used to be considered blood gills are now known to take no part in respiration; their function is to absorb mineral salts from the water.

Some chironomid larvae prey on other small invertebrate animals, seizing prey with their strong mandibles and swallowing them whole. Others scrape algae off stones or plants. The most interesting method of feeding is carried out by some larvae that spin funnel-shaped nets at the ends of their tubes. With rhythmic movements of the body they then create currents in the water which bring food particles into the net. From time to time they eat the net and its contents.

The pupae of chironomids are similar to those of mosquitoes except that instead of the breathing tubes on the head they have tufts of filaments capable of extracting oxygen from the water. These enable the pupae to remain at the bottom of the water or in the old larval tube until the time of emergence approaches, when, because of the air that has collected under the cuticle, they float easily to the

Adult drone fly, *Eristalis*

surface for the final transformation into adults.

The blackflies of the family Simuliidae are major pests of cattle in other countries and transmit a number of human and animal diseases, but they are only of minor importance in Britain. The larvae congregate on stones and plants in fast streams, attached to silken webs by hooks at their rear end. They are about 10mm (²/₅ inch) long and have two large mouth-brushes with which particles of debris carried down by the current are trapped and passed to the mouth. The pupae make cases shaped like an icecream cone and carry two bunches of respiratory filaments which project out of the top of the cases. More than enough air for immediate use is collected by the filaments, so when the adult fly emerges from the pupal case it rises to the surface of the

Pupa of rat-tailed maggot, *Eristalis*

Caddis, *Silo*, parasitised by the ichneumon *Agriotypus*

Fairy fly (ichneumon), *Caraphractus*

water in a bubble of air and can fly away immediately, its wings unwetted.

Flies in the sub-order Brachycera (Greek *brachys*, short) are called 'short-horns', as they have short antennae with only two or three segments. They include the soldier flies of the family Stratiomyidae, so named because the colouring of some of them − broad yellow bands, across a black body − resembles the gold and black military uniforms of more colourful days. The adults are usually seen resting on waterside plants, or perhaps sip-

ping nectar from the flowers in summer. From eggs laid on the plants, legless larvae with bodies tapering towards the tail-end appear in early summer. They hang from the surface film by means of a tuft of branched filaments which open out into a funnel, at the base of which are two spiracles that take in air. When a larva sinks down into the water a bubble is enclosed in the filaments to provide air while it is submerged. Microscopic animals are taken for food. When the larva is full-grown it is about 50mm (2 inches) long. It is difficult to tell when the insect has pupated, except that the larval case now floats horizontally at the surface. The pupa, in fact, occupies a small space at the front of the old larval skin and in due course the transformation to the adult fly takes place there.

The last of the sub-orders of Diptera is Cyclorrhapha, insects also with short antennae and stout bodies. The larvae are popularly called 'maggots'. The common house flies and their relatives are terrestrial members of this sub-order. One family, Syrphidae, includes the hover flies, some of which look remarkably like bees, with yellow and black bodies and a similar habit of hovering over flowers or in woodland clearings in summer. Some of them mimic various species of bees and wasps and thereby escape capture by predators. The adults of one group so closely resemble the drones of the hive bees that they are called drone flies. *Eristalis tenax* is the best known species and its larva is the remarkable rat-tailed maggot found in the mud of shallow ponds rich in decaying matter where it finds its food. When full-grown, it is about 15mm (³/₅ inch) in length and dirty-white in colour. At the rear end of the body is the long extendible breathing-tube, which consists of three sections that can telescope into each other and so be adjusted in length to reach the surface while the animal remains in the mud. The end of the tube has water-repellent hairs to prevent water getting into the tube and in the middle of these are the openings to the spiracles.

A more transparent and yellower rat-tailed maggot is the larva of *Myiatropa florea*, which can often be found in garden water butts as well as in holes in trees that have become filled with dead leaves. Its breathing-tube can be extended very considerably.

The pupal stage of these drone flies remain in the larval skin. The only noticeable difference is that the pupa is smaller than the larva and has two breathing 'horns' at the head end through which it takes in air as it floats at the surface of the water.

**Ichneumon flies** The large order Hymenoptera, which includes sawflies, ants, bees and wasps, as well as ichneumon flies, has only a few representatives with aquatic stages. These are all parasitic on other insects. *Agriotypus* is a parasite of caddis flies and the tiny frail female crawls down into the water of fast streams and lays her eggs inside the pupal cases of three kinds of caddis: *Goera*, *Silo* and *Odontocerum*. The larval ichneumons feed on the pupae of the caddis, but do not necessarily kill them. Caddis that have been attacked can be detected by a long, hollow silken tube projecting from

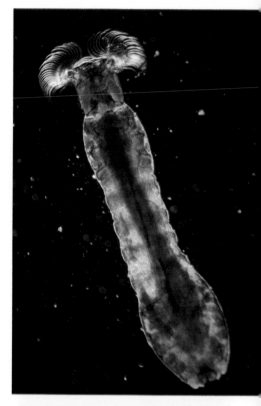

Above A water spider's air bell

Opposite (top) Larva of a blackfly, *Simulium* sp.

Opposite *Simulium* pupa

Right Water spider, *Argyroneta aquatica*

the caddis case. This is an extension of the pupal case made by the parasite and probably acts as a 'lung' to provide it with oxygen. The parasite remains in the pupal case as an adult during the winter and emerges the following spring.

Three species of parasitic wasps called chalcids lay their eggs in those of aquatic insects. The parasites are only about 1mm ($^1/_{25}$ inch) long and are sometimes called 'fairy flies'. *Caraphractus cinctus* lays its eggs singly in those of water beetles, while *Prestwichia aquatica* chooses beetles and bugs, such as water boatmen and water scorpions. *Diapria* is a parasite of aquatic fly larvae, including the rat-tailed maggot.

**Spiders and mites** The last group of arthropods to be discussed is the class Arachnida (Greek *arachne*, a spider), which includes the spiders and water mites. For convenience, a group of small animals that was formerly included in Arachnida but is now placed in a class of its own, Tardigrada, the water bears, will be mentioned briefly.

Arachnids have four pairs of legs, in contrast to the insects, which have only three, and the body is divided into a fore-part called the cephalothorax, combining the head and thorax, and the abdomen. They have no antennae.

The only spider that lives all the time in the water is the water spider, *Argyroneta aquatica*, which is found in weedy ponds and ditches in most parts of Britain. Average-sized specimens are from 8mm to 15mm ($^1/_3$ to $^3/_5$ inch). Unlike most spiders, the males are larger than the females and thus escape the risk run by most male spiders of being eaten by the female after pairing. The water spider is an air-breather that has adapted to an aquatic existence by making a bell-shaped air store under water in which to live. The spider first spins a flat web among water plants. Then, with repeated visits to the surface, it brings down air bubbles trapped by the hairs on its body, especially on the abdomen. By stroking these areas with its legs it dislodges the bubble, which rises under the web until eventually it becomes bell-shaped. Once the bell is made it does not need frequent replenishment, as oxygen diffuses into it to make up for that used in respiration and carbon dioxide diffuses out and dissolves in the water. Occasionally, however, the spider brings down a supply of fresh air from the surface. It lives in the bell except when capturing small animals for food, but takes the prey back into the bell to eat it. In summer the females lay between fifty and a hundred eggs, which they enclose in a silk bag, sealed off at the top of the bell.

Young spiders at first use empty snail shells for a home, but some climb out of the water and float away on lines of gossamer. The chance of finding a new pond or ditch must be remote, but a few must survive.

A number of spiders live around water. Of these the most striking is *Dolomedes fimbriatus*, called the 'raft-spider' because of an old story of one that floated downstream on a raft of leaves tied together with silk. 'Swamp spider' and 'fisher spider' have been suggested as more suitable names, as it lives in swamps and on the margins of drainage dykes and has been seen catching small fish by dabbling a leg in the water while standing at the water margin, then grasping them when they come within reach. Its usual method of hunting is to rest on floating leaves with one or two front legs touching the water to detect ripples caused by the struggles of insects that have fallen there, then rush over the surface to capture them. It can, however, pursue prey under water, too. *Dolomedes* is our largest spider, reaching a length of 18mm (nearly $^4/_5$ inch), and can be recognised by the two whitish stripes extending all the way along the dark, chocolate-brown body.

Water mites constitute a sub-order, Hydracarina (Latin *acarus*, a kind of mite). Over 300 species occur in Britain, and some are found in most ponds or streams. Although they are very small, ranging in size from less than 2mm to about 8mm ($\frac{1}{12}$ to $\frac{1}{3}$ inch), many of them are brightly coloured and so are easily seen. Red is the commonest colour, though there are also brown, green and bluish species. Some swim actively, but others crawl about water plants or on the bottom mud. They are all carnivorous and prey upon water fleas, chironomid larvae and aquatic worms.

The eggs are usually deposited on submerged stones or plants and covered with jelly, but some species embed them in the stems of submerged plants. The larvae, which have only three pairs of legs, are usually parasitic on insects and many may be found together on a single insect. Some species living in streams, however, do not lead parasitic lives.

Tardigrades (Latin *tardus*, sluggish; *gradior*, to walk), are microscopic in size, between 0·3 and 0·4mm long, and seventy-six species have been recorded in Britain. They are usually found accidentally when examining aquatic mosses or algae with a microscope, but the best way to discover them is to squeeze mosses from the damp margins of a pond or bog pool into a small dish and let the water stand for a time. If you examine the sediment you will probably see tardigrades, along with rotifers. Their slow movements, from which they are named, and the long claws on the legs reminded the early microscopists of a bear and the popular name 'water bears' has been given to them ever since.

From the mouth a pair of stylets can be thrust into the cells of plants to suck out their contents for food. The females produce up to thirty eggs, some species depositing them in the skin they have just discarded after moulting. The species of the genus *Macrobiotus*, especially *M. macronyx*, are the most likely tardigrades to be found in and around ponds.

## Vertebrates

To complete the survey of animal life in and around ponds and streams brief mention must be made of the vertebrates or backboned animals, and the part they play in the economy of these habitats. They include fish, amphibians, reptiles, birds and mammals.

**Fish** Representatives of several families of fish that are mainly marine have taken to living in fresh water, though freshwater fish do not form a separate division of the class Pisces. A few, such as the eel, salmon and sea trout, still spend much of their life in the sea. Our eels begin life in the Sargasso Sea, near Bermuda, where both the European and American eels spawn. The larvae are so unlike adult eels that for a long time they were thought to be a different kind of fish, named *Leptocephalus brevirostris*, and they are still called leptocephali. They are flattened from side to side and transparent, and at first are only 7mm (¼ inch) long. It takes them three years to cross the Atlantic Ocean and on reaching European coastlines become elvers, with round bodies about 65mm (2½ inches) long. They enter rivers on the west of Britain from January to March and on the east a little later, then find some suitable stretch of water in which to live. They are not deterred by polluted water and, when older, even cross land to get from one stream to another.

Eels feed on a wide variety of prey, including frogs, fish, crayfish, snails, and even small mammals and birds. The colouring of adult eels varies with their age. Through most of their period in fresh water they are grey or brown above and yellow underneath – the so-called 'yellow eels'. When they are fully mature (between four and ten years old) they are between 50–150cm (20–60 inches) long, the females being the larger. At this stage the underside becomes silvery in colour, with a metallic sheen, and they are known as 'silver eels'. About September or October they head for the sea, but their subsequent movements are a mystery, for adult eels have never been caught outside coastal regions.

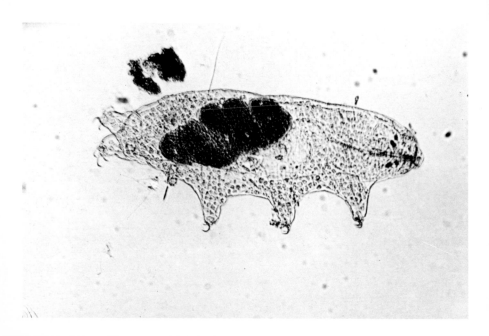

**Above** Water bear, *Macrobiotus* (highly magnified)

**Left** Water mite, *Hydrachna globosa*

**Below** Larval mites attached to a great diving beetle

Parr stage of brown trout

The Atlantic salmon carries out a migration the reverse of that of the eel, living its adult life in the sea but returning to breed in fresh water – indeed, in the very stream where its life began. During their adult life salmon travel widely in search of rich feeding grounds. Many travel to the waters off Norway, while others cross the Atlantic Ocean to western Greenland. The large number caught off Greenland is a threat to the survival of the species.

On their return to fresh water, usually in the autumn, the fish are fat and in prime condition after feeding on the rich supply of food in the sea. In their subsequent stay in fresh water they do not feed at all and yet, oddly, they will snap at the angler's lure, presumably in a reflex action at a moving object. After entering a river, they swim far upstream, often having to overcome obstacles such as weirs and small waterfalls. The chosen spawning areas, or redds, must have gravelly bottoms and a moderate current. With vigorous movements of their tails, the females scoop out a hollow and lay their eggs. The males lie alongside them as they do so, and eggs and milt (sperm) are shed into the redd. Several spawnings may take place at intervals over several days, the females covering each batch of eggs with gravel.

After spawning both males and females are called 'kelts'. They are exhausted and many die, but the survivors make their way back towards the sea and once in coastal waters feed and restore their condition so that in a year or two they may return to breed.

The eggs hatch in April or May and the young 'alevins' depend for food on the yolk sac on the underside of their body for about six weeks. When this supply is exhausted they catch minute animals and at this stage are known as 'fry'. At eighteen months or a year the young salmon will be about 150mm (6 inches) long. The parr marks – the vertical bands of dark colour on each side of the body – will be disappearing and they are then known as 'smolts'. At any time between two to four years the smolts move downriver to the sea and the rich source of food that it provides. Some may return to breed after only one year and are called 'grilse', but the majority stay four or five years, or even longer, before returning.

In the sea they feed mainly on fish such as herring. Adult salmon may reach a length of up to 150cm (60 inches) and a weight of 38·5kg (85lb).

Sea trout, which are simply a migratory variety of brown trout, have a similar life-history to that of the salmon, except that they feed while they are in fresh water. In contrast, the non-migratory brown trout do not pass through the silvery smolt stage as do sea trout and salmon. They are sedentary fish remaining in one favoured place, perhaps in the shelter of the bank of a stream or stones. Brown trout need well oxygenated and cool water to thrive and so have thus suffered from the pollution of many of their traditional habitats. Indeed, large numbers have had to be bred artificially and re-introduced in order to keep traditional trout streams stocked. When young, trout feed on insect larvae, water beetles and crustaceans, mostly as the prey drift past them downstream. Later they eat almost anything they can catch, including aquatic insects, freshwater shrimps and smaller fish. Their growth depends largely on temperature and is therefore faster in the south of the country than in the colder north. Southern chalk streams particularly favour rapid growth, for reasons that are not entirely clear. A full-grown trout may be 100cm (39 inches) long and weigh 15kg (about 33lb), but the British rod-caught record is 19lb 4½oz (8·745kg).

The rainbow trout, a native of North America, can tolerate higher temperatures and poorer quality water than the native trout; it also grows much faster. For these reasons many are now reared and introduced to fishing waters. Rainbows are also farmed extensively for human consumption. Although this fish was introduced to British waters as far back as the 1880s, few natural rainbow populations exist, as they rarely breed successfully in the wild in Britain and many of those that have been introduced have migrated to the sea.

A stream fish that is intermediate between the game fish and salmonids and the coarse fish is the grayling. Spawning as it does from March to May, it is attractive to the fly fisherman because it extends his season after the date when trout can no longer be fished. Grayling thrive in fast-flowing waters and take the same kind of food as trout. They grow to a length of between 25 and 50cm (10 to 20 inches) and the overall appearance is of a greyish fish with silvery sides and underparts.

The close seasons, when game fishing is not allowed, cover the periods when they are breeding. For salmon the close season in England and Wales is from 1 November to 31 January; for trout 1 October to the last day of February. There are local variations, however, and in Scotland the close seasons vary from river to river.

Turning to the coarse fish, most of those living in ponds and streams belong to the carp family, which includes gudgeon, tench, minnow, chub, dace, roach, rudd, bream and bleak. The carp itself, however, is a fish more characteristic of lowland lakes and rivers where there is abundant plant life, and many such waters are stocked with large specimens for angling. Formerly, though, carp were kept in great numbers in monastic and manorial stew ponds and moats to provide fish for meatless days. Their importance declined after the Industrial Revolution, once steam trains could bring adequate supplies of sea fish to towns for human consumption.

The roach, too, is more at home in larger habitats, but because it is an adaptable fish, tolerating mild pollution and low oxygen levels, it is probably the most important fish in the economy of ponds and canals. It will eat

Pike

almost anything (both animal and vegetable) and because it is a favourite with anglers, has been introduced into many freshwater habitats. Usually it grows to a length of 15 to 20cm (6 to 12 inches). It is an attractive fish with a dark grey back, silvery sides and with colourful fins – brown dorsal and tail fins, and red anal and pelvic fins.

Perch are undoubtedly our most handsome fish, with their bold body stripes, red anal and pectoral fins, and sharp-spined dorsal fins. They are sedentary fish and are found mainly in lakes, ponds, canals and slow-flowing rivers. The eggs are laid in long sticky ribbons which the female winds round water plants and stones. As many as 300,000 eggs may be laid by a large female. Perch grow to a length of between 15 and 30cm (6 to 12 inches). The larger individuals feed on fish, but smaller specimens eat insect larvae, freshwater shrimps and some plant material. Perch are more likely to be seen in spring and summer, when they often swim in shoals in shallow water. In winter they move to deeper water.

The gudgeon lives at the bottom of swift-flowing streams. It has a long, slender body and may grow to a length of 20cm (8 inches).

It is brownish above with a silvery underside. A distinctive feature is the pair of fleshy filaments (barbels) hanging from the corner of the mouth. Spawn is attached in clusters to stones and weeds. Gudgeon feed on creatures living at the bottom of the water such as freshwater shrimps, worms and insect larvae.

Tench are found in both still and flowing waters and prefer a muddy bottom and plenty of weed. They grow to a length of 30cm (12 inches) or more and are usually brownish-green on the back, with yellowish underparts. Two small barbels hang from the mouth. Tench can tolerate water with a low oxygen content and are resistant to fungal and other diseases. This is probably due to their very slimy skin, which in former times led to the tench being called the 'doctor fish'. It was believed that the slime possessed healing properties if rubbed on the human skin, while fish-farmers kept tench with their other fish because they thought that by rubbing against the tench their stock would be kept free of disease. Tench feed by rooting in the mud for worms and midge larvae and inevitably swallow a good deal of mud and detritus. Much of this passes out of the fish's digestive system and in this way tench help to keep ponds clean.

**Above** Roach        **Below** Perch

**Above** Smooth newts (male above)      **Below** Palmate newts (male above)

Minnows are familiar little fish in the well oxygenated waters of fast streams and are often seen in shoals. They are 10cm (4 inches) long when full-grown, greyish-green on the back shading to silver below. Irregular dark stripes or spots are conspicuous along the sides of the body. They feed mainly on midge larvae and small crustaceans, but occasionally eat plant material.

Although pike are more typical of lowland rivers and lakes, they are sometimes introduced by anglers to large ponds and canals, where they become the ultimate predator, eating other fish, waterfowl and small aquatic mammals. Lying in wait among vegetation, they attack any prey that comes within reach. Young pike feed on crustaceans and insect larvae, with the occasional small fish, frog or newt.

Two interesting little fish found in fast streams are the stone loach and the bullhead or 'miller's thumb'. They hide under stones and so need looking for. The stone loach is only about 10–13cm (4–5¼ inches) long, with an elongated body, dark green or blue-black above and light brownish below. The distinguishing feature is a number of barbels, one pair of long ones and two pairs of shorter ones, hanging from the mouth. Dark speckles cover the whole body, including the fins.

The stone loach needs well oxygenated water, but when it needs to supplement the supply it rises to the surface and swallows air. The air passes right through the fish and later bubbles emerge from the anus. When these bubbles have been analysed it has been found that oxygen has been extracted and carbon dioxide added, showing that the air swallowed has supplemented the oxygen obtained in the ordinary way through the gills.

Stone loach feed on the usual bottom-living animals such as freshwater shrimps and insect larvae. They are also known to eat fish eggs.

The bullhead is about the same length as the stone loach, but has a flattened body with a large head. It is protectively coloured to resemble the background: either dark brown or grey with darker blotches. There are spines on the gill-covers which can inflict a painful wound if the fish is handled carelessly. Their food is similar to that of the stone loach.

Finally, sticklebacks are of especial interest for the nest made by the male from plant debris, glued together with a secretion from his kidneys. One or more females are persuaded to lay their eggs in the nest, but the male alone guards the eggs and the young, when they hatch, chasing away possible predators and retrieving in his mouth any young that have strayed from the nest. Both the three-spined stickleback and the smaller ten-spined stickleback live in both still and flowing water. The former species is also found in brackish water or even in the sea.

The coarse fish close season, from 15 March to 15 June, covers the period when most of them are breeding.

Although some coarse fish, such as the roach, feed on plants as well as animal prey, pond and stream fish are mainly carnivorous and so, because of their size compared with the invertebrate animals, are important predators of them.

**Amphibians**   Present-day amphibians (Greek *amphibios*, leading a double life, that is on land and in water), are descended from fish-like ancestors that colonised dry land, but they still have to return to the water to breed. Although the adults breathe atmospheric air the larvae of newts and at first the tadpoles of frogs and toads have gills to enable them to absorb dissolved air from the water. There are three species of newts, one frog and two toads native to Britain.

The common, or smooth newt is about 10cm (4 inches) long. Although drably coloured when on land, in spring when it enters the water to breed the male becomes much more handsome with light upper parts spotted with black, red or orange underparts and a high crest along the back and tail.

The palmate newt is slightly smaller at about 75mm (3 inches), and even in the breeding season it has only a very low crest. The male, however, can then be distinguished by the short filament to the tail and the webbing of the toes in the hind feet, from which it is named. The females of these two newts are not easy to distinguish, but usually the throat of the palmate has no spots on it.

The crested newt is easily distinguishable. It is much larger, reaching a length of from 130 to 150mm (5 to 6 inches), its skin is rough and warty and the male has a magnificent crest. The undersides of both sexes are orange-coloured, liberally spotted with black.

On returning to the water in spring, newts indulge in a short period of courtship, then the male deposits a transparent capsule of sperm on the bottom of the pond which the female picks up with her vent to become fertilised. The eggs are attached singly to the leaves of water plants, the leaf being bent over to protect the egg. Egg-laying usually starts in April and may continue until July. The tadpoles are not like frog tadpoles but resemble miniature copies of the parents, except at first they have no legs and bear three pairs of external feathery gills throughout their tadpole stages. Front legs appear first, followed by back legs at about the eighth week. They leave the water usually about August, though some tadpoles which for some reason, such as food shortage or late hatching, do not develop by then remain in the water until the following year.

Both adult and larval newts are carnivorous. When in the water, the adults feed on small crustaceans, aquatic insect larvae, molluscs and tadpoles. Their tadpoles eat similar fare, but of course smaller specimens. On land, worms, slugs and insects are the chief prey of newts.

When winter approaches, newts hibernate in holes in the ground or under logs and stones. Some even creep into the cellars of houses.

There is only one native frog, the common or green frog. However, two continental species have been introduced: the marsh frog, which is found in drainage dykes in the Romney marsh area of Kent, and the edible frog, which has had small populations in various parts of southern England. As it is a more aquatic species than our own native frog, it is less easy to see, for it disappears into the water when approached.

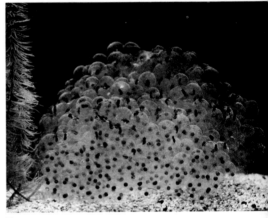

Frogspawn

Frog tadpole with external gills

**Above** Frog tadpole before the legs appear

**Right** Frog tadpole ready to leave the water

**Below** Toadspawn

**Above** Great crested newts (male above)    **Below** Common toad

**Above** Tadpole of smooth newt          **Below** Edible frog

The common frog returns to the water from hibernation earlier than the newt and in some years large masses of frogspawn may be found in sheltered places as early as January, though March and April are more usual. While the female lays her eggs, the male, mounted on her back, deposits sperm over them. The tadpoles take about twelve weeks to develop into froglets, at first eating algae attached to plants or stones. Later, when they need animal protein, they often eat the dead remains of unfortunate members of their own kind. A few days after the tadpole hatches from the egg external gills develop on the sides of the head, but soon they become covered with a fold of skin which encloses them to form a gill-chamber and they shrivel up. Oxygen is then absorbed from water taken in at the mouth or nose and passed over internal gills, the used water leaving the body through a small hole on the left side of the head. Towards the end of the second month of development the tadpole changes from a fish-like animal to an air-breathing creature, when its lungs come into use and it has to rise to the surface to breathe atmospheric air. The hind legs, which appeared first, are now supplemented by forelegs and the tail begins to shorten and is eventually absorbed into the body. The froglet leaves the water and makes quickly for cover in the surrounding vegetation at the waterside.

Toads are more choosy in selecting their sites for spawning, often returning year after year to a traditional pond that has been used by generations of toads. In this migration from their winter quarters they may die in their hundreds if the route crosses a busy road.

There are two native species of toad, the common toad of our gardens, and the natterjack toad, which has become an endangered species as its habitats in coastal sand dunes are rapidly being taken over for housing developments, holiday camps, military occupation or recreational purposes.

The eggs of both species are laid in long chains, those of the common toad being wrapped round water plants. But as plants are absent in the sandy pools in which the natterjack spawns, this is rarely possible for the natterjack toad. Sandy pools tend to dry up quickly and the metamorphosis of the natterjack tadpole is completed in a shorter time than that of the common toad – six to eight weeks, instead of nearly three months. Otherwise the development of toad tadpoles is similar to those of frogs.

The tadpoles of frogs and toads provide an abundant food supply for the other carnivorous inhabitants of ponds and slow streams during the summer months. Of the immense number of eggs produced by these amphibians, very few complete their full development to adulthood.

**Reptiles** The grass snake is the reptile most frequently seen in water, although both the viper, or adder, and the rare smooth snake swim occasionally. Frogs and newts and their tadpoles, as well as small fish, are the staple diet of the grass snake and in search of them it swims actively with a sinuous motion, with its head just above the surface.

**Birds** When considering the part birds play in the economy of ponds and streams it is easy to think only of those species that have a close association with water, such as ducks, coots, moorhens, swans, herons, kingfishers, dippers and wagtails. Much of the food of these birds is obtained in and around the water, so their presence affects the plants and animals living there. We tend to forget that all birds visit ponds and streams to drink or bathe and can play an important part in the dispersal of freshwater animals and plants both locally and, in the case of the migratory species of birds, over wide areas and even continents. The uniformity of freshwater organisms over the surface of the Earth may, indeed, be due to the ease with which eggs, resting stages and ephippia of crustaceans,

**Above** Natterjack toad       **Below** Common toads in amplexus

statoblasts of bryozoans, gemmules of sponges and similar objects adhere to the feet of birds or to their plumage, in the mud that covers them after a bathe or drink.

Great numbers of seeds of water plants such as bur-reeds and pondweed have been found in the crops of wild duck and experiments have shown that some seeds which have passed through the digestive tracks of water birds have germinated better than those that have not done so. The importance of such birds in distributing water plants must be very great.

Naturalists are also sometimes the unwitting distributors of freshwater organisms if they omit to wash out their collecting nets between visits to different ponds.

**Mammals**  Mammals, too, visit ponds and streams to drink and bathe and perhaps play a similar part in distributing aquatic organisms – but, since they do not make long-distance journeys, their effect is limited.

The otter, now a threatened species, acts purely as a predator, but not only of game fish, as is often thought. It also eats trout eggs and ailing fish and does a useful service by catching eels, which can be pests in rivers.

The water vole, which is common in slow streams and drainage dykes, is purely a plant-eater, choosing grasses and the stems and rhizomes of marginal plants. Its only misdemeanours are occasional damage to the banks of streams, canals or dams caused by burrowing.

The water shrew is by no means confined to watery habitats and is often found in woodlands, but it does frequent clear and unpolluted streams and ponds and eats a wide range of animals, including molluscs, insects and crustaceans, small fish and amphibians. It also becomes the prey of larger fish as it swims in the water.

# 5 FRESHWATER ECOLOGY

The inhabitants of a freshwater habitat are affected by many factors. Some are physical, such as temperature, light and the acid or alkaline content of the water. Others – referred to as 'biotic factors' – arise from relationships with other living things, as competitor, predator or prey. The impact of these factors varies even between different parts of a pond, so it is usual in studying the plant and animal life to consider the habitat as a series of zones.

In Chapter 3 we saw how, when you look at a pond, you at once notice that the plants are not indiscriminately placed, but are arranged roughly in distinct zones: namely, marsh plants, swamp plants, floating plants and plants that are totally submerged. This zoning reflects the plants' degree of adapta-

Figure 1

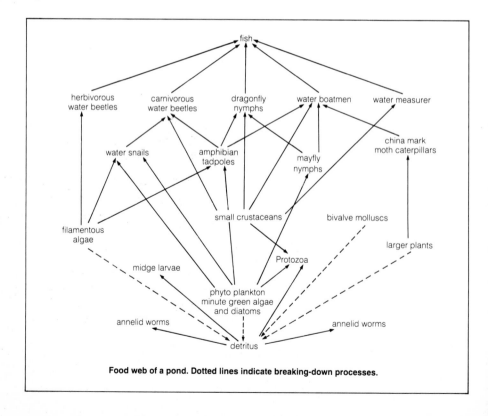

**Food web of a pond. Dotted lines indicate breaking-down processes.**

tion to aquatic life. In practice, botanists study this succession of plants from the opposite direction – from the open water, instead of from the bank – and call it a hydrosere (Greek *hydor*, water; Latin *sero*, put in a row). The first to colonise a stretch of water are the submerged water plants, such as Canadian waterweed and water milfoil. They can only occupy shallow water, as they need plenty of light to grow well. Any silting of the pond at this point will raise the level of the bottom and allow plants such as water-lilies to grow, providing their leaves can reach the surface of the water. The floating leaves, however, shade out the original submerged species and cause more silting, preparing the way for tall, emergent plants such as bulrushes, reeds and

yellow iris growing in shallower water. Their dense growth dies down in winter to raise the level of the mud still further.

Eventually, as the succession progresses year after year, the water level is reduced, the plant zones penetrate further into what was previously the water area and a swamp exists where once there was a pond.

In subsequent years the succession may continue to a climax vegetation of land plants. If the soil is sufficiently alkaline this will result in a fen, with grasses, sedges and eventually alder trees and willows. In acid conditions, the succession may be to bog mosses and sphagnum; and, if the area is wet, it remains a sphagnum bog. In drier conditions heath plants, such as ling or heather, and bilberry

Zonation of water plants

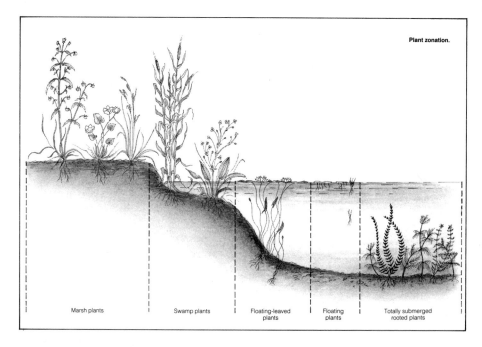

Plant zonation.

| Marsh plants | Swamp plants | Floating-leaved plants | Floating plants | Totally submerged rooted plants |

Figure 2

appear and eventually trees such as silver birch, pine and oak.

Turning now to the ecology of animal life in still waters, it is possible to distinguish four main zones of life:

> **the surface film**
> **the plant zone**
> **the open water**
> **the bottom mud.**

**The surface film** This strange habitat, midway between air and water, has been adopted by a number of small insects well adapted to survive there. Pond skaters, water measurers and water crickets all find a rich supply of food there, with little danger of predation. One has only to watch the surface of a pond on a summer day to realise how many small flying insects fall or settle on the surface and are unable to take off again. These soon become the prey of the three groups of water

bugs, who impale them with their beak-like rostra and suck out their body fluids. Whirligig beetles, too, exploit the same source of food and can also chase prey below the surface. The tiny springtails make do with smaller fare, pollen or other vegetable matter that is blown onto the surface. Some of the small rove-beetles, which are not aquatic insects but live near water and frequently fall on the surface, make good their escape in an interesting way. From the rear end of the body they produce a liquid which lessens the surface tension of the water and enables them to propel themselves to the safety of the bank. Since the underside of the surface film can support small objects, mosquito and gnat larvae and pupae rest there effortlessly while taking in air.

**The plant zone** At the pond margins, extending out towards the middle of the pond, is the richest growth of water plants, providing abundant food for the herbivores, which in turn makes it a rich hunting ground for carnivores. Snails, caddis larvae, china-mark moth caterpillars and pond mayfly larvae feed on the plants; and water beetles, water bugs, dragonfly larvae and leeches feed on them. Oxygen is abundant due to the photosynthesis of the plants. It is this zone that is the busiest part of the pond.

**The open water**  Away from the busy margins, the relative quiet of the middle of the pond is the home of both the largest and smallest members of the community – the fish and the planktonic plants and animals, including the minute crustaceans and rotifers that feed on the abundant microscopic algae.

**The bottom mud**  Surprisingly, this seemingly unsavoury region of the pond has probably the largest animal populations in the pond. The chironomid larvae, including 'bloodworms', live in immense numbers in little silken shelters in the mud, recycling plant and animal debris which has fallen to the bottom, and tubifex worms may also be there in quantity. Both kinds of animal, one an insect larva and the other a true worm, have haemoglobin in their blood and can make do with the limited supply of oxygen left after bacteria have broken down the detritus into simpler substances. Pea-shell cockles and (in larger ponds) freshwater mussels live embedded in the mud and filter out organic particles from the water. Water lice, too, are commonly found here, scavenging for food.

A slow stream, ditch or canal has zones across it similar to those of a pond, but it is usual to regard the zonation of a moving water habitat as running along its length, each stretch of the watercourse having its characteristic communities.

The kind of plants and animals that can live in such conditions depends largely on the nature of the stream bed, which in turn is determined by the speed of the water flowing over it. In hilly districts where the gradients are steep the current may be so strong that all smaller particles are swept rapidly downstream and the bed will consist of bare rock, with a few large stones sheltering patches of gravel. In sheltered places plant life will be restricted to a few mosses and liverworts and a coating of algae on stones. Underneath the stones will be some kinds of stone flies and mayflies, the latter with much flattened bodies which enable them to live closely pressed to the surface of the stones, offering very little resistance to the current, their strong claws holding firmly onto the stones. In these turbulent streams a few species of caddis fly larvae are found too, some of which make cases of small stones in which to live, fastening them securely to the stones. Others do not make cases but spin funnel-shaped nets, with the open end facing upstream to catch small particles of food swept downstream.

In recent years it has been discovered that some of these stream insects leave the security of their hiding places at night to feed and inevitably drift downstream. This 'drift fauna' is now known to be an important part of the diet of fish characteristic to these fast streams, such as trout.

It might be wondered why animals live at all in such precarious surroundings but there are some compensations. Water in streams is usually better oxygenated than in ponds, for it is cooler and can hold more oxygen. Also, the oxygen dissolves more readily when the surface of water is disturbed, as it is when flowing and splashing over stones. It is no use bringing back small animals from fast streams and expecting them to survive in an aquarium unless it, too, has cool and well aerated water.

In lowland districts and in the lower reaches of hill streams, where the gradient is not so steep, the flow of water is slower. As a result, silt and smaller stones are no longer swept relentlessly along and can be deposited on the stream bed to provide a root-hold for water plants. Here there is more food for small animals, so different species exist in these slower streams. In bends of the stream even more silt is deposited and conditions more like a pond occur. Here even water-lilies may be found, along with many other plants characteristic of still waters. Water beetles, water boatmen, caddis larvae, with cases made of plant materials, and dragonfly nymphs may be among the fauna of these quieter reaches.

Eventually the stream empties into a lake, river or pond, or directly into the sea. When it comes under the influence of tides, the variety of living things decreases, for few species can survive the daily surge of salt water. Those that can – the brackish water fauna – are especially interesting, as they show how freshwater animals may originally have come from the sea and adapted to a new environment.

By now it will be abundantly clear that a pond or stream contains more than a random collection of plants and animals. It is a community of interacting organisms which has evolved over a long period of time so that its members are living in some sort of ordered relationship between themselves and their environment.

Ecology is the study of plants and animals in relation to their environment and a pond is probably the best habitat in which to carry out this study. It is the nearest approach to a closed environment that can be found, with

Figure 3

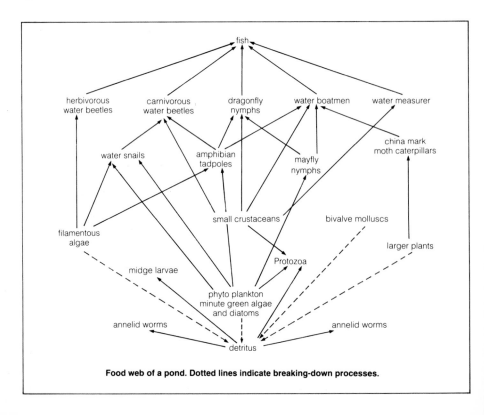

Food web of a pond. Dotted lines indicate breaking-down processes.

very little interference from outside influences. It is, in fact, a microcosm, a world in miniature, in which all the elemental forces are apparent and can be observed.

The interrelationships of living things in any habitat turn on two basic principles: a continuous flow of energy through the system and the cycling of matter. The starting point of the flow of energy is sunlight, which enables green plants, the *primary producers*, to convert simple chemical substances into organic compounds which, as food, provide the plant-eating animals or herbivores, the *primary consumers*, with the energy they need for their life processes. They in turn are eaten by the carnivores, the *secondary consumers*. Finally, all plants and animals die eventually,

and the bacteria and fungi take over as *decomposers*, break down the remains and recycle them into simple inorganic substances that can be used again by more green plants.

This transfer of food energy from plants through a number of animals is called a food chain, and it is an interesting exercise to work out a number of food chains from personal observation, based on the simple pattern:

green plant → herbivore → carnivore.

The number of individuals involved at each stage is smaller as the organisms become larger. Thousands of single-celled algae are needed to feed hundreds of water fleas, but a single fish can soon eat all the water fleas. This phenomenon is known as the pyramid of

Figure 4

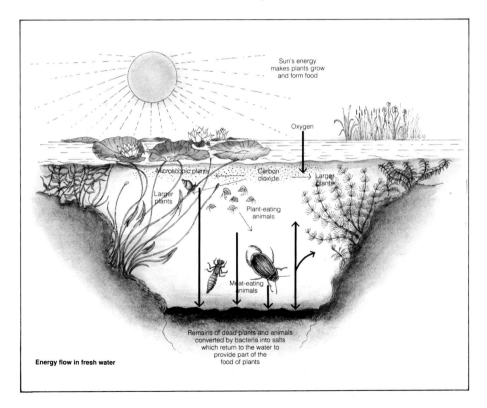

Sun's energy makes plants grow and form food

Oxygen

Microscopic plants

Carbon dioxide

Larger plants

Larger plants

Plant-eating animals

Meat-eating animals

Remains of dead plants and animals converted by bacteria into salts which return to the water to provide part of the food of plants

**Energy flow in fresh water**

numbers – the pyramid's base being the vast number of algae, the apex the single fish.

Frequently, consumers eat more than one kind of food. A fish such as a roach may feed on both plants and animals. Food chains, therefore, link up to form complicated food webs, and these are a more accurate representation of the relationships existing in a pond. A typical, simplified food web of a pond is shown in Figure 3. An even better representation of the factors at work in a freshwater habitat is an energy flow diagram, showing both building-up and breaking-down processes, and taking into account materials such as drainage waters entering the habitat and the adult stages of animals leaving it. A simplified example is shown in Figure 4.

# 6  STUDYING FRESHWATER LIFE

The immense variety of plants and animals living in ponds and streams has always attracted amateur naturalists and in recent years their numbers have been greatly augmented by classes and courses from schools and colleges. It is disappointing to find that few of these excursions into the countryside are more than collecting trips or proceed far beyond the stage of seeing what each lucky dip with a net brings forth. Yet a little planning and a more systematic approach can benefit both the fauna and flora and the students themselves.

## Avoiding damage

The loss of freshwater habitats has made it necessary to adopt a much more responsible approach to field work if certain species are not to be threatened or lost. Observation of a few simple rules can prevent much damage:

1 If possible, examine all larger specimens at the waterside and return them as soon as possible to the water, having made field notes.

2 If specimens are essential for further study, take no more than are necessary, keep them in cool, shady conditions, use adequate containers in which to transport them, and return them as soon as possible to the original habitat.

3 If you are conducting a party, appoint one person to be responsible for specimens and their return.

4 If stones or logs are turned over in the water in searching for specimens, remember to turn them back again or the animals that live underneath may die.

5 Water plants that have been taken out so that they can be examined for specimens must be returned to the water.

6 Avoid trampling the ground along the pond and stream margins, and leave the habitat as you found it.

7 Always ask permission from landowners or occupiers to study on private land.

## An ecological survey

One positive approach to pond or stream studies is to make an ecological survey. Such a survey, carried out over a long period, can be of the greatest value to county trusts for nature conservation and similar bodies that own or manage nature reserves. In basic terms, the purpose of an ecological survey is to find the answer to five questions: what lives where, when, how and why?

The first question can be answered by finding and trying to identify accurately the plants and animals in a habitat. This is probably the hardest of any survey, for correct identification of some groups is difficult and in some cases – caddis larvae, for instance – almost impossible at present.

It will be necessary to search in all the four zones of a pond – surface film, plant zone, open water and bottom mud – to answer the question 'Where?' Time, in relation both to seasons and also to the time of day, is an important consideration. The larvae of many insects, such as beetles, bugs and dragonflies, are more abundant during the summer months, whereas those of stone flies and mayflies in streams have mostly left the water by then and are at their most numerous during the winter. Daily movements of water fleas and other small animals take place. During a part of the day they may congregate near the surface and at another they will be nearer the bottom.

The question of how organisms live where they do calls for a study of their modifications and adaptations, and can best be undertaken at home or in a laboratory. The modifications of bodily structure or in behaviour which enable different creatures to use atmospheric air even when living under water are especially relevant.

Lastly there is the fundamental question 'Why?' What advantages does living where it does afford a particular species? A more abundant food supply than on land must have caused some secondarily aquatic animals to return to water. Small invertebrates that are always in danger of drought on land escape that risk in water.

A detailed survey of a stream will very soon reveal whether it is suffering from pollution or eutrophication and routine monitoring of streams is carried out by regional water authorities and others for this purpose. Sampling the animals on the bottom of the stream gives a good indication of the degree of pollution. The first species to disappear are the larvae of stone flies and mayflies. With greater pollution, caddis larvae disappear and, of course, fish such as trout, grayling, chub and dace. As pollution increases, freshwater shrimps, water lice, leeches and most snails are absent, and, when pollution is so bad that little oxygen is left in the water, only red chironomid larvae and sludge-worms, which have haemoglobin in their blood, can exist.

Without laboratory facilities, testing the chemical content of streams is difficult, but indicator papers, available from pharmaceutical firms, give a rough idea of what is present in the water. Turmeric test paper turns brown when ammonia is present; lead acetate paper turns black with a high concentration of hydrogen sulphide, the gas produced by the decay of living things. The alkalinity or acidity of the water can be ascertained approximately by a range of pH papers.

More accurate estimations of the degree of pollution of a stream can be made by determining the amount of oxygen taken up by bacteria in bringing about the decomposition of the polluting material. This, called the biochemical oxygen demand, or BOD for short, is measured by the amount of oxygen taken up by 1 litre of the effluent at 20°C in five days. Some schools and colleges may be able to carry out such an investigation in a stream survey.

# Equipment

Elaborate equipment is not needed for freshwater studies. Some kind of net is essential, and suitable ones with strong iron frames with a diameter of 23cm (9 inches) are available from dealers in natural history supplies. For studying small forms of life a plankton net is needed. The net material is usually a fine-meshed nylon material and ideally should have a mesh of 180 per 25mm (1 inch) for microscopic algae, or 60 per 25mm for small animals in the plankton. The tube or bottle at the bottom of the net should be of plastic rather than glass to avoid breakages when it hits stones. After sweeping a plankton net through the water for a few times, allow about a minute for the catch to be concentrated in the tube. Examination with a lens magnifier of about × 5 to × 8 is adequate. Lenses of higher magnification will not allow examination through the whole width of the tube.

If the net can be removed from the stick, lines can be fastened to it so that it may be towed through the water as a drag net. A metal kitchen strainer tied by its handle to a strong stick makes a useful cheap net.

Plankton net

A kitchen sieve can make a useful net

When using nets in a stream, place the open end facing upstream; animals disturbed from the stones will then be carried into the net by the current.

An enamel or plastic meat tray or similar flat container is needed for examining the catch. The contents of the net are emptied on to the tray and it is then easy to see what has been captured. With a small paint brush or wide-mouthed pipette any specimen required for examination can be transferred to another vessel of water. If an eye-dropper type of pipette is being used, reverse the tube so that the narrow end is in the teat and the full width of the tube can be used to pick up the specimens.

Air-breathing insect larvae should be carried in wet weed in containers rather than in jars of water, since jolting of the water in transit can break up the surface film and prevent them breathing.

As soon as you arrive home or at the

laboratory, empty the catch into large, shallow dishes, putting each species – or each specimen, in the case of carnivorous species – into a separate container. For observation purposes, plastic sandwich boxes with lids are ideal if furnished with a layer of gravel and a few pieces of water plant, and a stone or two for animals that live or hide under stones.

A microscope is an almost essential piece of equipment for the serious student but the cheap variety obtainable in gift shops and some camera shops should be avoided, as they are optically very poor and they use non-standard lenses so that they cannot be added to as experience is gained and more powerful objectives are needed. The best kind to buy is a stereoscopic microscope in which both eyes are used; and one giving magnifications from about × 10 to × 50 is adequate. These are not very expensive – in fact, they are often cheaper than a reasonable pair of binoculars.

With the more powerful monocular microscopes, sometimes called 'student microscopes', specimens need to be prepared as microscope slides before examination, whereas with the lower power stereoscopic microscopes specimens in water can give endless pleasure without any preparation.

# FURTHER READING

Books are listed under two headings: identification manuals and books for general reading which give fuller details of the life histories and biology of the plants and animals.

## Identification manuals

The scientific publications of the Freshwater Biological Association include many on identification but they do require a knowledge of technical terms. At present they include publications on the following groups: Cladocera (water fleas), copepods, larger crustaceans (Malacostraca), water snails, leeches, planarian worms, annelid worms, rotifers, bryozoans, amoebae, stone flies, mayflies, adult caddis flies, caseless caddis larvae, water bugs, alderflies and sponge flies, adult chironomid flies and freshwater fishes. A complete list will be sent if a stamped addressed envelope is enclosed with a request to the Librarian, FBA, The Ferry House, Far Sawrey, Ambleside, Cumbria LA22 0LP.

Other identification guides include the following:

Belcher, H., and Swale, E., *A Beginner's Guide to Freshwater Algae* (Institute of Terrestrial Ecology/HMSO, 1976).

Belcher, H., and Swale, E., *An Illustrated Guide to River Phytoplankton* (Institute of Terrestrial Ecology/HMSO, 1979).

Clegg, J., *Observer's Book of Pond Life* (Frederick Warne, 1980).

Haslam, S., Sinker, C., and Wolseley, P., *British Water Plants* (Field Studies Council/E. W. Classey, 1975).

Macan, T. T., *A Guide to Freshwater Invertebrate Animals* (Longman, 1959).

Muus, B. J., *Collins Guide to the Freshwater Fishes of Great Britain and Europe* (Collins, 1971).

Quigley, M., *Invertebrates of Streams and Rivers: A Key to Identification* (Edward Arnold, 1977).

## General reading

Angel, H., and Wolseley, P., *The Family Water Naturalist* (Michael Joseph, 1982).

Clegg, J., *Freshwater Life* (Frederick Warne, 1974).

Hynes, H. B. N., *The Biology of Polluted Waters* (Liverpool University Press, 1960).

Leadley-Brown, A., *Ecology of Fresh Water* (Heinemann Educational, 1971).

Macan, T. T., *Ponds and Lakes* (Allen & Unwin, 1973).

Macan, T. T., and Worthington, E. B., *Life in Lakes and Rivers* (Collins, 1971).

Mellanby, H., *Animal Life in Fresh Water* (Methuen, 1963).

Mills, D. H., *An Introduction to Freshwater Ecology* (Oliver & Boyd, 1972).

Taylor, Ron, *Ponds and Streams*, Look-out chart handbooks (Concertina Publications, 1979).

Thompson, G., Coldrey, J., and Bernard, G., *The Pond* (Collins, 1984).

The majority of these books should be obtainable from public libraries.

# INDEX

liver fluke *Fasciola hepatica* 45, **46**
liverworts 13, 25, 33, 115
 common *Marchantia polymorpha* 33
 floating crystal *Riccia fluitans* 33
 great scented *Conocephalum
  conicum* 33
 wide-nerved *Pellia epiphylla* 33
loosestrife, purple *Lythrum salicaria*
 15
*Lophopus* 55, **55**
louse, freshwater 14, 45
*Lumbriculus* 49
*Lymnaea pereger/peregra* 45–46, 56
 *stagnalis* 56, **58**
 *truncatula* 45–46, 56

*Macrobiotus* 97, **98**
*Macrobiotus macronyx* 97
Malacostraca 64
malaria 36, 40, 90
mammals 97, 104, 111
March Brown 69
*Margaritifera margaritifera* 59
marsh marigold (kingcup) *Caltha
 palustris* 15, **15**
mayflies 68–69, **70**, 78, 115, 120
meadowsweet 15
medusa *Craspedacusta sowerbii* 41, 44
Megaloptera 66
*Micrasterias* 32
*Microhydra* 44
*Microstomum* 45
midges 49, 67, 90–91, 104
miller's thumb 104
minnow 48, 100, 104
mites 13, 59, 96–97
*Molanna angustata* 80
molluscs 35, 56–59, 60, 111
moorhen 109
mosquitoes 40, 67, 73, 89, **89**,
 90–91
moss animals 9, 13, 20, 35, 54–55
mosses 13, 25, 33, 115
 bog (sphagnum) 33, 113
 long-beaked water feather 33
 willow 33, **33**
moths 67, 79, 115
mussels 13, 35, 47, 56, 58–59,
 115
 duck 59
 painter's 59
 pearl 59
 swan **57**
*Myriatropa florea* 94

Naididae 49
Nematocera 89, 91
nematocysts 42
*Nemoura cinerea* 68
*Nepa cinerea* 74
Neuroptera 66

newts 104–105, 109
 common smooth *Triturus
  vulgaris* **103**, 104, **108**
 great crested *Triturus cristatus*
  105, **107**
 palmate *Triturus helveticus* **103**,
  105
*Nostoc* 28
*Notonecta* spp 76
*Nymphula nymphaeata* 81, **81**

Odonata 66, 69
*Odontocerum* 94
 *albicorne* 80
oligochaetes 49
*Ophydium* 40
orl fly 78
*Oscillatoria* 28
*Osmylus* 66
ostracods 61, **62**
otter 111

*Paramecium* **38**, 38–39, 43
*Paraponyx stratiotata* 82, **82**
perch 47–48, 52, 101, **102**
*Perla* 67
*Perla bipunctata* 68
phantom midges 90, 91, **91**
*Philodina roseola* 52, **53**
Philoptamidae 80
*Phryganea* 80
Phryganeidae 79–80
pike 47–48, 52, **101**, 104
Pisces 97
*Piscicola geometra* 52
planarians 44–45
plankton 37, 60
 net 120, 121, **121**
*Planorbarius corneus* 56, **58**
*Planorbis crista* 56–57
*Plasmodium* 36, 40
Plectoptera 66
*Plumatella* 55
*Polycelis felina* 45
 *nigra* 45
Polychaetes 49
*Polymorphus minutus* 48
Polyphaga 82, 85
*Polystomum* 45
polyzoans 52, 54
pond skaters 9, 73–74, 114
pondweed 111
 broad-leaved 20
Porifera 41
*Potamophylax stellatus* 80
*Potamopyrgus jenkinsi* 57
*Prestwichia aquatica* 96
proboscis roundworms 48–49
Prosobranchia 57
Protista 37
*Protonemura meyeri* 68

Protozoa 13–14, 29, 33, 35–37,
 39–40, 54
Pterygota 66
*Ptychoptera* spp 89
Pulmonata 56
Pyralidae 81
*Pyrrhosoma nymphula* 72

raft-spider 96
*Ranatra linearis* (long water
 scorpion) 75, 96
rat-tailed maggot **93**, 94, 96
reed, common **18**, 113
reedmace *see* bulrushes
reptiles 97, 109
rhabdocoeles 45
*Rhabdolaimus* 47
*Rhithrogena haarupi* 69
Rhizopoda 37
*Rhyacophila* 80, **81**
*Rivularia* 28
roach 45, 47, 100–101, **102**, 117
rotifers 27, **27**, 33, 35, 52–54, **53**,
 115
roundworms 13, 47–49
rudd 100
rushes 15

*Salminicola salmonea* 61
salmon 52, 61–62, 97, 99–100
*Saprolegnia* 26, **26**
Sarcodina 37
saucer bug **74**, 75–76
sawflies 94
*Schistocephalus gasterostei* 47, 61
schistosomes 47
sea-anemones 41
sea louse 63, **63**, 64
sedges 15, 80–81, 113
*Sericostoma personatum* 81
sewage fungus 14
Sherry Spinner 69
short-horns 93
shrimp, fairy 60, **60**
 freshwater 26, 48, 59, 64, **64**,
  100–101, 104, 120
*Silo* **93**, 94
*Silo pallipes* 80
Simulidae 92–93
sludge-worms 14, 120
smooth snake 109
snails 13, 20, 35, 45–47, 56–58,
 65, 97, 120
 pond 56, **58**
 ramshorn 56–57, **58**
 river (freshwater winkles) 57, **58**
snakes 109
soldier flies 93
*Sphaerium corneum* 59
spiders 13, 59, 96
*Spirogyra* 29–30, **30**, 32